# SONGS OF THE SEA

# SONGS OF THE SEA

TERRY L. KINSEY

ROBERT HALE · LONDON

© *Terry L. Kinsey 1989*
*First published in Great Britain 1989*

Robert Hale Limited
Clerkenwell House
Clerkenwell Green
London EC1R 0HT


British Library Cataloguing in Publication Data

Songs of the Sea.
 1. Sea Shanties in England. Collections
 I. Kinsey, Terry L.
784,6'86 23 8

ISBN 0-7090-3696-5

Photoset in North Wales by
Derek Doyle & Associates, Mold, Clwyd.
Printed in Great Britain by
St Edmundsbury Press Ltd, Bury St Edmunds, Suffolk.
Bound by WBC Bookbinders Limited.

# Contents

# Dedication

My years of collecting shanties, forebitters and ballads have now come to an end. They began as long ago as 1957, with weatherbound British yacht crews entertaining themselves to an impromptu shanty evening in Ostende. The audience and participators grew as overseas crews joined in and added their own ballads, which proved to be much akin to our own. The language of the sea and the sentiments, hopes and aspirations of seafarers proved to be international.

Since then I have collected sea-songs from all the oceans and seaboards bordering those oceans but principally from a group of not-so-young seafaring 'gentlemen' who sailed the Horn, screwed cotton and raced the tea- and wool-clippers home. Sadly their numbers steadily diminished but in the fuggy atmosphere of waterside taverns, where they could still see the navigation lights of ships making their way to distant waters, they recalled to me the 'for instances' and sang in broken voices the ballads they thought they had long forgotten.

The hard winter of 1981 saw my last two 'gentlemen' 'a-going out wi' the tide', as they would so matter-of-factly have put it, within days of each other. And there my collection ends.

This book is a tribute, lest we forget, to the men of iron who sailed ships of wood with sails of cloth, for their like we may never see again.

# 1 Introduction: A Revival

Running up Channel recently on a lonely night passage, the pre-dawn mist found me in the middle of an overtaking fleet of Tall Ships, making for Spithead on one of their two-yearly passage races. Ghosting past close alongside, the *Norsaga* began setting more sail on her massive yards to the chanting of a shanty. The words were foreign, but the beat was familiar and the purpose obvious. The crew, young and old, weak and strong, boys and girls, untrained and inexperienced in the ways of sea and ships, were working in perfect unison, keeping in time by the beat of their singing, to hoist the cloud of sails on the massive yards by concerted muscle-power, utilizing simple rope purchases and whips.

Later that same year, I was spectator to the young crew of an Ocean Youth Club yacht, singing with vigour the shanties by which they worked their boat, to an enthralled audience in the open air, on the harbour wall in Copenhagen. More recently, during a visit to an Outward Bound Sea School, I was again spectator and also participant at an evening of shanties provided by a local folk-group which was greeted by an enthusiastic and vigorous response from students and instructors alike.

This enthusiasm of the shanty-singers and the fascinating melancholy of their songs I found infectious, and I was determined to rediscover and collect as many shanties and sea-songs as I could. I thought I'd find thirty or so, but the extent of this book shows I badly misjudged the numbers of shanties which were created and sung in the great period of sailing-ships.

The revival of shanty evenings now occupies a sociable part of many a yacht club's winter activities, and with such celebrated recording groups as 'The Spinners' adding shanties to their repertoire and cutting shanty discs and tapes, universal interest has been aroused not only in the songs but in the men who created and sang them in the situations that warranted their creation and use.

In my search to rediscover and collect old shanties I learned much more than harmonies and ballads: I found that the songs are stories of man's relationship with the sea, of how he grew to understand it and to use it for his own ends. They relate tales of courage and daring and immense hardship. I also learned the stories behind the shanties and about the life and times of the singers, their hopes and aspirations, their loves and their fears, whether they were Sailor Johns or Naval Tars, and this I have used to try to capture the atmosphere and conditions in which the songs were sung.

# 2 What, Why, Who

## What Are Shanties?

Shanties are tuneful, rousing songs with a pronounced beat, sung by sailors at their work – they are, in fact, work-songs. Although records show the earliest shanties as being well over 200 years old (one, 'Lowlands', was sung on Sir Walter Raleigh's ship), the most creative period of shanty-singing was between 1820 and 1850.

The simple rhythm of the shanty can in some respects be compared with the strict rhythmic songs of the army, but while the latter were used to enforce discipline, encourage the weaker to keep up and ensure a regiment's arrival as a fighting unit at the end of a hard day's march, the rhythm of the shanty was primarily to unify the effort of a group of individuals and harness their collective muscle-power to move enormous loads easily, quickly and safely by the crudest of machines–windlasses, capstans, blocks, tackle and whips. Shanties fall into separate well-defined categories, differing in rhythm and timing: some long and repetitive for capstan-hauling, others having a short, jerky delivery for hand-over-hand-hauling or pumping, while others incorporate action words which were shouted for the 'stamp-and-go' long-hauling.

The criteria which underlined the earliest of shanties were that they were rhythmic and tuneful with simple words that were easily remembered, for the men were for the most part illiterate and often slow to learn. The music was not scored, so the learning of the tunes and the words was by rote, and the passing-on of tunes from one

11

generation to the next was by word of mouth.

The shanty is not to be confused with another type of sea-song, the forebitter, although the two cannot be divorced and both are recorded in this book. The forebitter is a simple sea-song or a ballad usually with a nautical flavour, sung for entertainment during the off-watch period of the second dog-watch. The forebitter gained its name from the fact that the sing-song would usually take place on warm tropical nights in the open air around the forebitts, close to the capstan or windlass. In bad weather the singers would gather beneath the forecastle to sing for mutual companionship.

In the later eighteenth century, as the seamen's lot improved, it was possible for the larger ships to boast a 'fu-fu' band to accompany the singing of forebitters. This would possibly comprise a concertina, fiddle or tin whistle to provide the tunes to the improvised accompaniment of a rhythm section made up of spoons, cazoos, drums made out of animal bladders and knick-knacks (animal bones, usually rib bones, held between the fingers and clicked in rhythm) and hardwood slats used for the same purpose.

## The Shantyman

The selection of a shanty to accompany a particular task, and the leading of the singing, was primarily the duty of the shantyman. He would sing the verse and stamp or beat out a rhythm, frequently improvising it to suit the task, while the crew joined boisterously rather than tunefully in singing the choruses and heaving and hauling on appropriately shouted words.

The shantyman was a person of some importance aboard ship, especially if he had the added talent of being able to scratch out a tune on a fiddle (which he would probably have made from an old cigar-box), blow a tin whistle or squeeze a concertina. However, many a shantyman held his position not because of his melodious voice and sense of music but because he could bellow loudly, stamp or beat out a rhythm and be heard above the shriek of the wind, the thundering of the sails and the sound of a big sea running hard alongside. On the ship's muster book he would be entered as being an 'idler' – not meaning a person lacking industry or prone to laziness but one having no watch-keeping or station-keeping responsibilities on board ship. He was excused all heaving and hauling work, or, if he actually did tail onto a rope or breast a capstan bar, he would exert only token effort so as to save his wind for shantying, for he was there solely to organize the working parties by his choice of shanty to suit the task and by concerting their efforts by singing the shanty verses. His other shipboard duties would be of a non-seamanlike nature, possibly as the captain's steward, 'cookie's mate' or 'chippie's louse'.

## The Origins of Shanties

The exact origin of the word 'shanty' is lost in the mists of history, but a number of theories have been put forward, any one of which may be correct.

One simple theory is that the word originates from the old English word 'chant' or 'chaunt' – to sing. Its origin may be French, however, from the French verb *'chanter'*, – to sing – the French too, were a considerable seapower, and their seamen were very little different from the British. Another theory suggests that 'shanty' may have come from the bawdy-houses and drinking dens found in the seaports of the Gulf of Mexico, the West Indies and the Caribbean where seamen would gather together between cargoes and sing drinking-songs: as those dens were called 'shanties', it is not unreasonable to suppose that the term 'shanty songs' may have had its origin there.

Another possible origin is in the West Indies. The majority of West Indians lived in shanty huts bordering the sea, made of light bamboo, washed-up planking and anything that came to hand. These huts were regularly moved from place to place or into sheltered positions when hurricanes and tidal waves were imminent. Wooden rollers would be inserted below the hut, several families and friends participating, and the hut would be heaved and hauled to its new site. The chant leader who would organize the working parties would sit athwart the ridge of the roof of the shanty and sing out local songs while the hauling parties joined in on the choruses, while working in unison.

From the earliest days of the buccaneers, the West Indian Negro has served aboard British ships, both merchant and naval, and he figures prominently by name in many a shanty. Going to sea in foreign ships was a major occupation for the menfolk of the West Indies. Negroes have a great reputation for their sense of rhythm and for singing and dancing, and homeward-bound ships were usually well crewed by Negroes as replacements for men who had been killed by accident or by privateers or who had been lost at sea or had died from various illnesses and fevers along the journey. Many a ship's crew comprised at least half Negroes, and in those ships a 'chequerboard watch' system was introduced. Unlike today, with the three-watch system, the crews would be divided into two watches (port and starboard), one watch comprising white seamen, the other black seamen. This system worked very well, not because of racial division but because one watch would compete with the other for sharpness and efficiency. Friendly rivalry in off-watch singing and entertainment also emerged.

The Negroes were undoubtedly a creative source of many shanty tunes themselves, being used to singing while they worked in the cane-breaks or picked cotton on the slave plantations, and later when working in the railroad gangs. Negroes are a naturally musical people, and it is still common to hear them singing work-songs whenever two or more are working closely together.

Even today, new shanty tunes are still coming out of the islands, and as recently as 1981 a long-playing record was made containing such songs as 'Judy Drownded', 'Angelina', 'Day Ho' and the 'Banana Boat Song'. These are updated versions of the old working-day songs – the simplicity of beat, tune and words stamps them as a modern application of the shanty.

A timely reminder that shanties did not die with the demise of the great sailing-ship era was to be seen at Cowes Week during the 1980 season, when a thirty-two-foot cutter, double-banked on her eight oars, was rowed about assembling racing-craft each day and pulled in perfect unison by a crew hauling in strict tempo to the tune of 'Sailing' – a popular recording at that time. Although the purist will dispute that that tune is a shanty, its simple, swinging rhythm made it ideal to harness the muscle-power for the task, and so to all intents it can be regarded as a work-song. In the same way, 'Old Portsmouth', another popular modern tune, can also be regarded as a forebitter (a leisure-time ballad, not a work-song) by virtue of its being a simple, repetitive tune with a good rhythm suitable as a hornpipe.

Leisure-time dancing was encouraged in the false belief that, the more a body was physically engaged, the less chance there was of its contracting illness as the red corpuscles chased the white corpuscles out of the system. So dancing for the seamen and 'skylarking' (playing tag, catch-as-catch-can and races through the rigging) for the ship's boys were encouraged and taken seriously as an anti-scorbutic.

## The Evolution of Shanties

In order to appreciate the purpose of the shanty, to recognize the varying rhythms of the different types for the various tasks they served and to understand from them the messages they carried and the record of the lives lived out by the common sailorman, it is important to give the reader some impression of the seamen themselves and of the harsh environment in which they lived. Thus the first part of this book sets out to examine the life and times of the people who found it necessary to create shanties and of the purpose to which the shanties were put. The final part presents a collection of shanties and other sea-songs, for not all the sailors' songs were work-songs, and these have been arranged and grouped together under the heading of the tasks by which they would have been sung.

Some of the earlier shanties sung on merchant ships were undoubtedly borrowed and adapted from the King's Navy, where shantymen occupied a jealously guarded station on board ship. This influence was probably due to the fact that many merchant ships – such as the famous Blackwall frigates, the Honourable John Company's ships (East Indiamen) and privateers (fast, heavily armed ships sailing under Letters of Marque and Reprisal) – were run along the lines of the men-o'-war of the King's Navy.

Having difficulty in finding musical scores and original lyrics for a number of the shanties, I am grateful to the many ageing sailormen who with great patience put up with my badgering them to recall and sing shanties which they thought they had long forgotten. They recalled for me many songs sung by their grandfathers and even their great-grandfathers, and by their singing them they gave me the opportunity to set down many simple harmonies and refrains. A number of these shanties are well over a century and a half old and are remarkable not only in withstanding the passage of time without written record but in withstanding the past century or so, when the very environment in which they were used has long been surpassed and mainly forgotten.

It is even more remarkable to find that a number of shanties are still taught to children in school today and that the melodies can often be heard hummed or sung by many who have not the slightest interest in the sea. A number of examples spring to mind: 'Billy Boy', 'Rio Grande', 'A Roving' and 'Shenandoah'.

The nineteenth century was probably the most popular period for shanty-singing, for great fleets of sailing-ships pursued their business in this their heydey before steamships began to take over. The volume of sailing-traffic was quite staggering. The historian Major E.C. Cooper, a reliable maritime authority, wrote of coastal traffic along the East Anglian coast: 'In October 1838 there were nearly 2,000 vessels lying windbound in Yarmouth Roads. They got under-way on 1st November and were followed by another 1,000 from the southward; in all 3,000 sails went through the Roads in five hours, so that the sea could hardly be seen for ships.'

The major happenings of the time proved the inspiration of many of the shanties. The French wars gave rise to 'Boney Was a Warrior' and 'Blood Red Roses'. From the American Civil War came 'The *Alabama*', and Britain's Jack Tar quickly put his own words to 'Marching Through Georgia', 'John Brown's Body' and 'When Johnny Comes Marching Home Again'.

The 1820s until the 1850s, including the period of the Irish Potato Famine and the great migration to America by the Irish, saw the introduction of the Western Ocean Packets sailing from Liverpool and Bristol – reference to the famous Black Ball Line and the Blue Cross Line recurs in a number of songs and the rise in the emigrant cargo is recorded in 'We're All Bound to Go' and 'The Packet Ship'. Many of the men who manned those speedy packet ships became known as 'Packet Rats' and were mainly of Liverpool or Irish descent – Liverpool and Bristol being the principal manning ports. The term acknowledged their craft as prime seamen and their tenacity in overcoming the elements to make fast passages, and was in fact a compliment as jealously guarded as was the term 'Desert Rats' in a much later turbulent period.

The emigrants and the Packet Rats were responsible for a whole range of new songs, such as 'Liverpool Judies', 'The Liverpool Packet', 'The Banks of Newfoundland', 'Paddy West', 'Paddy Doyle's Boots', 'Paddy Lay Back', 'Leave Her, Johnny', 'Blow the Man Down' and 'Can't You Dance the Polka'.

A further important period was the growth of the cotton trade around the confluence of the Mississippi, the Ohio and the Missouri rivers and Mobile Bay. This trade began during the 1790s, when the invention of the spinning-frame by Arkwright, the spinning jenny by Hargreaves, Crompton's mule and Cartwright's power loom made possible mass cotton-wear production in Britain which created an ever-growing demand for Southern States cotton. New ports developed and old waterside villages took on a new importance; New Orleans, Savannah and Mobile enjoyed this new prosperity and welcomed the ships and sailors with every sort of entertainment and amusement which would quickly transfer the wealth from Sailor Jack's pockets into their own.

It was in those ports that the sailors developed the new skill of cotton stevedores, or 'hoosiers', down in the holds of their own ships. There they worked side by side with the Negroes stowing the bales of cotton, known as 'screwing cotton', by forcing the bulky bales into every corner, between the ship's timbers and into each dark recess of the holds by means of great jack-screws. The Negroes chanted as they hove round the unwieldy jackscrews, and soon the sailors adapted their own capstan and windlass shanties to suit the task: 'Donkey Riding', 'Shenandoah' and 'Roll the Cotton Down' are examples.

This was the time before Samuel Plimsoll introduced his famous loading line bill in Parliament, and the cotton-carrying ships were jammed well above capacity by the forced-loading of the jackscrew. Cotton swells in the presence of moisture, and as the sea made easy ingress through the strained seams and forced deck planking which the screwing had created, a great number of these 'coffin ships' literally fell apart in mid-ocean and whole crews were lost. Popular shanties among the sailors at that time were 'Johnny Come Down to Hilo' and 'Clear the Track, Let the Bulgine Run', two shanties which demonstrate the co-existence of black and white seamen as words of Negro extraction had clearly been put to traditional Western rhythms.

When the Western Ocean vessels were not on the cotton run, the summer months would see them assembling as the Quebec Fleet. As the winter's ice retreated north to the Arctic Circle, they ventured into the great St Lawrence seaway, driving as far inland as Miramichi and Quebec. There they would load huge baulks of timber to the accompaniment of 'The Banks of Newfoundland', 'Donkey Riding' and other songs they had brought north from the Southern States. These songs were suited primarily to the rhythm of screwing cotton, but the hauling work necessary in the loading of trunks of timber through the bow loading-ports of the droghers had a similar rhythm, and many were adapted to suit the work.

1848 saw the west coast of America opened up by the finding of gold in Sacramento, California. Gold-fever grasped the venturesome, and any vessels that would float were chartered. No Panama Canal existed then, and everyone had to go by way of the dreaded Horn or alternatively disembark at Portobelo in the Gulf of Darien, then force-trek almost in the footsteps of Cortes through the swamp- and fever-ridden isthmus and across fierce Chagre Indian territory to Balboa in the Gulf of Panama, then take ship again. Round the Horn became the popular but no less risky route, as the bleached bones of the wrecks still bear testimony. Until then only the ships in the nitrate and saltpetre trade had ventured round the Horn, and then only along the coast of Chile as far as Valparaiso, but now everything was making for Frisco Bay and the new boom town of San Francisco. Soon new shanties were being sung, telling of the hardships suffered in the tempestuous Southern ocean and the Roaring Forties and along the western seaboard of Chile and California – shanties like 'Valparaiso Round the Horn', 'Sacramento', 'The Gals around Cape Horn' and 'Goodbye Fare-ye-well'.

The decline of the sailing-ship was now being felt. Steamships, powered capstans, steam windlasses and donkey engines were quickly changing the face of shipping and, as a result, the role of the sailor. The goldfields of Australia did not see as great a rush of diggers as the Californian rush and made no lasting impression on the 'flying-fish sailors', as the tea- and wool-clippermen called themselves, and probably the only true shanty to come out of Australia was the capstan shanty 'South Australia'. Although the pumping shanty 'Strike the Bell' has the same tune as 'Click Go the Shears', it cannot truly be said to be sailor-inspired by the seamen of the 'Stralian' run.

The opening of the Suez Canal in 1867 saw the 'damnable tin-kettles' (steamships) taking over the China tea trade and the Australian wool trade. Although the clippers sailed with double crews so as to race the ship day and night to beat the steamships, they could not really compete, and so sadly the great sailing-ship era died, and with it faded the necessity to create new shanties as machinery began to take over the sailorman's work.

The sailor was not over-awed by evolution, however. It was constantly with him and had been all his working life, so he simply adapted to the changes with a typical seaman's phlegm. He had already seen the old-fashioned windlass superseded by the capstan, and he had simply altered the beat of the windlass shanty to meet the rhythm of capstan heaving and kept on working. He had changed, without too much regret, the old jerky backbreaking 'jiggity-pump' shanties to keep in time with the demands of the more modern flywheel-pump. The demise of the great square-riggers in favour of 'fore-and-after' rig for all but the great-circle passage-makers ('Lime Juicers' and 'South Spainers') saw the old 'stamp-and-go' shanties, which accompanied the crew's tailing onto the halyards and running across the deck hauling as they went, being adapted to the short, jerky rhythm suited to the hand-over-hand hauling which the lighter-sparred ships required.

Summing up then, shanties can be said to be one of the earliest and truest examples of folk-music, setting out simply and tunefully the hopes and aspirations of their creators, describing the important events of the times and leaving a melancholy record of the hardships endured by simple sailormen and their dependants in an illustrious period in Britain's maritime history.

## The Range of the Shanties

Fortunately, Sailor Jack sang of everything under the sun that caught his interest, endowing each tune with the particular slant of the seaman's philosophy.

He sang of far-off places. In the latter part of the eighteenth century, the major ports were the Cinque Ports (Sandwich, Hythe, Hastings, Romney and Dover) which, together with Harwich and many other small east- and north-east-coast ports were well placed for trade with the continent of Europe. The shanties of that period were reminiscent of places Jack had visited in the Old World – Amsterdam, Copenhagen, Lisbon, Cadiz, Naples, the Levant, the Barbary Coast, West Africa and the mighty Congo River.

With the opening of the New World in the late sixteenth century, the Cinque Ports and the smaller North Sea ports diminished in importance, except for North European trade, as they were situated downwind of the Atlantic. The harbours which lay at the western end of the English Channel soon developed in size and importance, for they were more convenient for an easy departure and a minimum of windward sailing against the prevailing westerly winds. Plymouth, Bristol and Liverpool took on the Atlantic and New World traffic and gave the sailors new places, names and characters to sing about, firstly Newfoundland, Boston and New York, then, as the adventurers, colonizers and traders moved south, New Orleans, Mobile Bay and Rio, and finally they circumnavigated the dreaded Cape Horn and sang about Valparaiso and 'Frisco.

Jack sang too of his heroes, real or legendary: Napoleon, Santa Anna (the last President of Mexico until his defeat in 1847 by another seaman's hero, the American General Taylor), John Paul Jones and Jean Lafitte, the American privateer sea-captains who gave British maritime commerce many a bloody nose. Jolly Jack and Sailor John's heroes were universal, and in their singing they honoured friend and foe with impartiality.

Jack even sang of Lizer Lee and many of the formidable Madams and their bawdy establishments, even though some of them were notorious 'crimps', relieving him of his hard-earned pay with one hand while collecting a 'percentage' for drugging him and despatching him to a short-handed ship ready to sail.

He sang always of his constant companions – unremitting hard work, bad weather, gales and fog, frost and snow, great calms, hunger and thirst, and of his lighter moments of love, the Bowery girls and the Spanish ladies with whom he caroused on his runs ashore. It is interesting to note that 'Spanish Ladies' dates back to the 1660s.

Jack sang of the ships he had served in and of their crankiness, of intolerant officers and god-aspiring captains, and of bullying bucko mates, while at the same time making light of stranding and shipwreck and even death itself. He was not irreverent about death and took great interest in seeing that the last rites were performed with due reverence before a dead colleague was put over the side, but, being on nodding terms with death each day, it held no fear for him.

Not all the sailors' songs were shanties, however, and many songs were sung when 'off-watch' for entertainment to lift the spirits and encourage mutual companionship on long, monotonous passages. These were the 'forebitters' (p.12) which resembled the army's camp-fire songs, such as this century's 'Tipperary' and 'Lily Marlene'. Sailor Jack too was often in need of morale-boosting, and the forecastle (or in the tropics the foredeck) often echoed to his melancholy, haunting songs.

During this period the bulk of the nation's commerce was handled by two principal areas – London for European, Mediterranean and East Indies trade, and Bristol and Liverpool for the Americas and the West Indies – and certain shanties were put to different melodies by London and Medway sailors, who sang one version, while the West Coasters sang to a different tune.

The shanties and forebitters of the seamen open a door and give us a fleeting glimpse, like a tuneful diary, of the life and times, events and aspirations of a time beyond the reach of memory, when Britain was stirred by mercantile enterprise and territorial conquest as she moved out of medieval isolation. The history books record the stirring events, the battles, the illustrious commanders, the victories, the conquests and the dates to be remembered, but the role of the common people has been ignored, although no period is more alive with incident and interest which by their efforts and suffering they helped to create.

Just as the sea closes swiftly round the ship's keel, and the fretful wash and wake vanish astern to leave no track of her passing, so without the simple words of the sailors' songs handed down through the generations by word of mouth to give us a human record, the passing of the great age of sailormen would show no ripple on the sea of Britain's achievements.

## The Creators of the Shanties

The days when men of iron sailed ships of wood with sails of canvas are gone for ever, killed off by the social advances of the Industrial Revolution, the building of ships in iron, the invention of the steam-engine and with it the steamship ('that ignominious monster of the water') and the development of the railroad.

The argument as to whether this was a good thing or not is not the concern of this book. One thing that is certain, however, is that a seafarer's life 200 years ago was one of unbelievable hardship, with clumsy and often unweatherly ships, overpressed and frequently unseaworthy, making great ocean passages in all seasons and in all weathers, usually overloaded and governed by greedy shipowners, and commanded by ruthless masters (many of whom had shares in the ship), tyrannical officers and bullying bosuns.

One cannot begin to describe the penurious life endured by the sailor's family ashore while the breadwinner was away for long years at sea, living and suffering conditions unfit for animals and all the time risking an untimely and horrific death. Yet this was the very period when, by the efforts of such seamen, Britain was at her greatest as a seafaring nation by exploration, trade and conquest, and it is just that the gallant and unrewarded enterprise of these men who rose to the challenge of a breathless period of opportunity should not go unrecorded.

The common sailorman's qualifications for a life at sea were his strength and physical fitness and a grim determination which would help him survive being constantly wet, cold, underfed and overworked. His inadequate rations would not maintain his strength on long passages, and a deficiency of fresh food saw him suffering from scurvy and other terrible diseases. Uneducated, illiterate and inarticulate he may have been, but he was not stupid, although many captains preferred to a number of obviously mentally sub-normal men on board, believing that their lack of mental capacity was made up for by extra physical strength and that they could be bullied into working harder and for longer periods. The sailors worked their ships with a will, fierce obstinacy and stoicism and with a surprising loyalty unfound in any other calling – except possibly that which the equally inhuman conditions of the Army and King's Navy of that period also created.

The passing of that period in Britain's history left behind the annexation of vast tracts of land enjoying the protection of the Union flag, the building of the Empire, the establishing of major trade routes, the creation of Great Britain's reputation as *the* major seafaring nation of the world both economically and militarily and yet left scant record of the common sailors who were instrumental in bringing this about.

However, they did leave behind the work-songs and forebitters which illustrate so simply and clearly their life and times of the 200 years ago. Using the words of their songs, they let us open a window on a period beyond living memory which we in this sophisticated age find hard to appreciate.

## The Seamen – Singers of Shanties

Just what did the sailormen have to endure during that period? Certainly conditions intolerable by today's thinking. The night before sailing, Jack would pack his sea-bag ('duffle'); sea-chests were for the afterguard who had something worthwhile to pack – Jack would think himself lucky if he had a change of clothing. He would be wearing his best shore-going clothing to impress the master as he presented himself to sign Articles, but his duffle would contain all the rest of his worldly possessions.

His sea-going clothing simply comprised rough sailcloth trousers, a coarse woollen shirt, neckerchief, canvas oversmock or leather sleeveless jerkin, leather belt, wooden or rope-handled sheath-knife and marlin spike. His heavy-weather gear, the forerunner of today's 'oilies', was simply an old jacket weather-proofed with daubings of pitch or made from tarpaulin. Underclothing and sleeping-attire were not for him, and he would go barefoot on deck.

He would have a pannikin (a metal bowl from which he both ate and drank) and would eat with his sheath-knife and fingers, though he might possess a fork or spoon if he had been skilful enough to whittle one from bone or wood.

He slept 'all-standing' (fully clothed) in coffin-like bunks fastened to the ship's side on a 'donkey's breakfast' (a palliasse or straw mattress) and covered himself with a square of sacking. While a few ships had hammocks, this was mainly a King's Navy custom, intended to crowd in their large crews throughout the equipment-packed gundecks.

Jack was deeply religious, smart and conscious of his appearance, bathing under the wash-deck pump and shaving once a week just prior to Sunday prayers conducted by the master. He kept a small sacking roll, which he referred to as his 'housewife', in which he kept his razor, needles, thread and wool, and when off watch he would take pride in patching, darning, sewing and even knitting. He made his own trousers from old scraps of weather-beaten sailcloth which he could scrounge from the sailmaker, as the well-used material would have lost its hardness and be less likely to chafe.

Headgear would range from 'Monmouths', felt hats, to

woollen caps and was an important part of a seaman's clothing. The older and more experienced hands possessed a wide-brimmed sennit hat, affording them shade from the fierce sun in the tropics, and for the bitter weather of the northern latitudes the more observant acquired a pair of worn-out leather knee-length sea-boots cast aside by an officer. The rough seaman's shirts, jerkins and trousers had no pockets, so tobacco and pipe, together with other small, valuable possessions were stowed inside the hat and were thus held secure and safe, although theft was a rare occurrence on board ship.

Tobacco was his only indulgence on board ship, smoked through a clay pipe. In the tropics, however, the tobacco was chewed, the fierce plug tobacco causing the mouth to salivate and relieve the pangs of continual thirst. A sailor was rarely without his pigtail of 'chawin' terbaccy'. Sailors' possessions were so meagre that at the death of a messmate they added to them by auctioning between them the dead man's possessions, pledging to pass the money on to the widow upon returning home.

There was no regular recruitment procedure for merchant seamen. Having heard that a particular ship was sailing on a certain tide, Jack would present himself on the day before sailing, hoping to be offered a berth. His wife and children would accompany him to the dockside to await the outcome.

On deck would be a table at which sat the captain, who might also be the shipowner, shouldered by the mate and an open muster book.

Presenting a written discharge from his previous ship which attested to his good conduct, his aptitude for work and his sobriety, Jack would await the captain's decision. Without a good discharge he would not have made it across the gangway, which was zealously guarded by the bosun. If accepted, he would be advanced one month's pay, which he passed across the ship's rail to his wife waiting below on the dockside. No contact with her, or with the shore, was now allowed, the brawny bosun on gangway duty saw to that, and this was the last Jack would see of his family, often for years, until he had earned a good discharge at the end of the voyage.

A good discharge was the prize for which he worked, for without it he could not get another ship, and with more seamen than berths, paupery was the only alternative for him and his family. The value of a good discharge was not lost on the captain and mate, and with this forever dangled in front of the sailors as bait, they could exploit them to the full. Blind obedience, servile humility, acquiescence to all demands, and watch-and-watch-about were the price of a good discharge.

Having passed his advance across to his wife, Jack would go below to the forecastle to change into his working rig. The forecastle was located right forward and as such was a most untenable place as soon as the ship cleared the shelter of the land. Driving forward in anything of a seaway, the bows would pitch into the oncoming seas, and the ship's seams would work and flex, so that sea-water squirted into the forecastle in a steady stream, while from the deck above the seas breaking inboard would be a constant downpour, soaking everything and keeping it wet for long afterwards.

There was no natural light between decks, for portholes and skylights were too vulnerable to the seas breaking inboard. Any light was from the hatchway or from horn lanterns lit by candles – these provided by the sailors themselves. Most ships went with unlit forecastles, as the risk of fire was too fearsome to risk.

Lord Runciman, the millionaire shipowner who started life by running away from home at Blythe to ship out as a cabin-boy in Northumbrian collier brigs, recalls the injustices of a coasting seaman's lot: '…the foc'sle used to open and shut like bellows and every plunge and roll she took, she gave the impression she was splitting in two …. These foc'sles were grim holes, with half-a-dozen hammocks swinging in the dark, dank space between cable locker and foremast, bumping with each roll into each other and into barrels of grease, tar and paint, anchor cables and dunnage dumped there ….' The sailors put these conditions to words in the ballad 'Salt Beef'.

The coasting seaman's lot was slightly better than that

of the crews of the deep-water South Spainers and West Indiamen, whose living-quarters were with the windlass under the 'top-gallant foc'sle head' on the forepart of the maindeck, with a roof overhead but with no real protection forward, where the anchor cables came through the hawse-holes, and completely open aft. Here men could be drowned and occasionally frozen to death while they slept.

Washing-facilities were a bucket of sea-water and sea-water soap and were the sailor's own responsibility. During the week he therefore often went unwashed whilst on passage and hoped to keep himself and his meagre clothing clean by the constant soakings he suffered while going about his duties. Toilet facilities were simply the 'bucket and chuck it' system, although after the Merchant Shipping Act of 1876 primitive 'thunderboxes' were used on a few ships.

Samuel Plimsoll's Merchant Shipping Act of 1876 did so much to improve conditions for seamen that Sailor Jack actually put his appreciation of it into the shanty 'According to the Act'. This very revealing ballad details with fair exactitude just what he could now expect in the way of rations and duty periods, and if these seem meagre enough, it is as well to remember these were the *improvements* 'according to the Act'.

For one improvement in conditions at sea the British sailor was derided by his American counterparts. They called him 'Limey' ('Lime Juicer'), as one of the stipulations of the Act ensured he had a regular supply of lime juice as a precaution against scurvy, a disease which comes from a continual diet of salt meat and no fresh vegetables.

Although the Act did undoubtedly help the sailors' welfare, the extreme conditions saw Jack suffering maladies within a week or so of leaving port. The first would be salt-water sores, big, open sores on the skin softened by constant immersion in salt water; boils followed and whole areas of flesh softened, swelled, broke open, putressed and became unbearable to the slightest touch. The task of working ship was cruelly hard, and the continual handling of tacks and sheets, heaving on capstan bars and heaving on coarse rope left raw gashes on softened fingers and palms.

The ships were woefully undermanned, and the hauling (pulling) and heaving (pushing – windlass, capstan bars and pump handles) needed so much effort that ruptures plagued most sailors, and there was no relief on board ship from the endless toil. Strangulated ruptures caused so much pain that it was common practice for the sufferer to hang upside down in the rigging and attempt to manipulate the protrusion back through the ruptured cavity. This may have relieved the pain temporarily but did nothing for the cause, and with the next exertion the condition re-occurred.

Wet clothes, wet bedding and the wet, cold and mildewy atmosphere of the forecastle caused chronic chest infections, and TB was rampant. Add to this the strength-sapping effect of bad food and scurvy, risk of accident, chance of being lost overboard, risk of injury or death by action of privateers and pirates, death by stranding and shipwreck and death by tropical diseases fever and cholera, and one wonders why men ever went to sea.

Today a sea-going ship is expected to have sonar to read the contours of the ocean floor, radar to penetrate darkness and fog, satellite navigation systems to pin-point a ships's exact latitude and longitude, automatic pilot to maintain an accurate course, and gyro compasses which are unaffected by the Earth's or ship's magnetism, up-to-date charts and pilot books, radio communication and RDF, and pilots to give first-hand guidance through troublesome stretches, while the coastline too, its approaches, dangers and safe channels, is well lit. Yet even today, equipped with all this technology, ships and sailors are lost at sea.

How much more hazardous was it then in the early part of our era and how much greater must have been the fear of the early sailors. They had no scientific understanding of the sea; the cause of the tides was a mystery, charts were non-existent, and the horizon marked the limit of their known world. For the sailors of northern Europe sea-voyaging was a particularly hazardous undertaking. The westerly winds that sweep in unhampered from the North Atlantic bring gales, storms, rain and poor visibility. The northerlies bring clear skies, but strong, cold winds, while the easterlies sweep in carrying the snow and icy cold of the Arctic in their grasp. There is none of the predictability of the Trade Winds found in the equatorial zones. In northern waters thick fog can descend in a moment and shroud the land and sea for days on end. Calms can last for hours. The sea too is very different. It is not clear and translucent, so that rocks, shoals and other hazards can be seen with the naked eye, but opaque with silt, hiding most dangers that lurk barely hidden beneath the surface. The sea is relatively shallow, and the tidal streams are strong and difficult to plot, particularly in the English Channel, Dover Straits, Bristol Channel and Pentland Firth – round most of the coast, in fact.

Signing on a superbly fitted-out ship with an experienced master and crew was no assurance of making a safe landfall or any landfall for that matter, even if it was only a few miles down the coast, as the wrecks around Britain's coast bear mute testimony. Charts either did not exist or were so primitive and inaccurate (being drawn 'by guess and by God') that they were a further hazard in themselves, often leading ships to their deaths.

Bearing all this in mind, accepting the terrible living-conditions and working for long hours on open weather-swept decks in all weathers, one wonders why men ever ventured onto the sea.

As if the above risks were not appalling enough, greedy shipowners could prove more deadly than all the rest put together. 'Coffin-ships' – rotten, unseaworthy vessels with no hope of surviving even moderate weather – were sent to sea over-insured by unscrupulous shipowners in the hope that they would founder, and many hundreds of sailors perished so that the owners could rid themselves of worn-out ships and claim the dishonest insurance – a practice known as 'barratry'.

One wonders why, having suffered such hardship,

dangers and privations and having survived, a sailor ever returned to sea a second time. In fact, while most sailors arrived home vowing 'never again' – as set to verse in the shanty 'Jackie Brown', generally Sailor Jack returned to sea bitterly disillusioned with his homecoming. In those days a sailor would be away for years at a time and naturally dreamed of a wonderful homecoming – the longer away, the more wonderful his imagination painted it. But as often as not the harsh reality of life ashore in a seaport for a common sailor's family fell woefully short of his expectations. He came home to abject poverty, sickness, indebtedness and squalid, insanitary, hovel-like accommodation, so he often sought refuge in drink, women and carousing, and as soon as his money ran out, so did the hostelers' hospitality, and the girls became unfriendly, so the sailor found himself longing for the sea again and signing on with the first available ship.

Unlike the Naval Tar, who was always confined to ship, the Merchant Jack enjoyed frequent runs ashore between discharging and taking cargo. He wasn't likely to 'jump ship', as desertion was called, for without his 'good discharge' he would literally be stranded high and dry in a strange country, for no reputable captain would ever again sign him on.

On shore Sailor Jack really lived up to his nickname, 'Jolly Jack'. Gone for a short time were the hardships of watch-and-watch-about, the dangers and risks, the thirst and bad food: he was out to show just what he was made of.

His shore-going rig, which he had last worn to impress the captain when he signed articles, would be rummaged out of his duffle and the wrinkles smoothed out. His sailcloth trousers would have been washed and liberally powdered with chalk so as to appear whiter than white, and the green mould sponged off his blue serge 'bum-freezer' jacket. His shoes and his hat, black, low-crowned, with a broad brim and newly tarred, would be given a rub with blacking (a mixture of fat and soot) and polished to a sparkling shine. Should he have acquired a pair of pinchbeck buckles for his shoes, he would have spit and polished them until they gave a fair imitation of gold. A pair of brass ear-rings would receive the same attention and be inserted just for the occasion – after all, he didn't want his ears to turn green. The trousers would be worn at least three inches above the ankles, to reveal cotton stockings, the brighter the better, even contrasting stripes; a similar gaudy neckerchief would add to the effect and brand him a seaman of substance.

So attired and with a seaman's roll and a jingle in his pocket, he would sally forth to show the port, its bawdy-houses and the ladies especially that the British merchant sailor was a special breed of seaman, while he himself was a 'flashman' and the best of the lot. He would carouse and drink and above all sing and would bring back on board amorous memories, empty pockets, a thick head and the songs he had learned, to add to his repertoire.

The seamen serving in the King's ships during this period cannot be overlooked either, for they shared the horrors and deprivations and sang more or less the same shanties and for the same purposes as their messmates in the mercantile fleets. But not for them the undermanned ships; quite the reverse – the press gang saw to that. Small warships such as frigates would carry 300 men, while a ship of the line would carry between 600 and 700 sailors and marines. The muscle work needed to sail the ship was none the easier for all the manpower, for the ships were bigger, with heavier gear and much more of it. Nor did Navy ships shorten sail during the night; they would be sailed hard day and night and in all weathers.

The Naval Tars lived herded together like animals between decks. Hammocks were slung in every available space, hammock touching hammock and one above the other, often with the underside of the one above rubbing the occupant in the one below – one restless sleeper would disturb the others around him.

Such conditions proved ideal hatcheries for disease and fever, particularly in the tropics, and records detail whole crews being wiped out by epidemics. The stench of bilge-water, the other shipboard smells and such closely packed humanity, especially in rough seas when all the gunports were shut tight, would turn the most hardened seaman's stomach so that he couldn't eat.

The casks of brackish drinking water soon turned foul, and unimaginable growths appeared; accounts describe the men closing their eyes and holding their noses before drinking their beaker of water.

Fresh meat and vegetables were exhausted within a few days of sailing, and salt horse (the term for any salted meat) and ships' biscuit were the staple food. Then, as now, the government imposed swingeing restrictions on dockyard spending, and the victuallers regularly under-packed or packaged rotten meat in the casks, while the cooperage of water casks was not properly maintained, resulting in fresh drinking-water being lost into the bilges. The always parched seamen would find it almost impossible to swallow the dry, rock-hard biscuit, and possibly the first ever blackmarket activities were recorded as the men would bribe the cook with favours and minor possessions, and even in extremity with their precious ration of rum, 'sippers' for small favours and 'gulpers' for larger ones, so as to be allowed to scrape from the sides of the meat cauldrons the solidified fat left over from boiling the salt out of the meat. This 'slush' as it was termed spread thinly on the biscuit would help it to become a little more palatable, or maybe it just greased it to slip down a little easier. It is interesting to speculate whether the term 'slush' and its implication has anything to do with the modern term 'slush money'.

With no provision for baking bread aboard ship, the biscuit was commonly referred to as 'ship's bread'. It quickly became wormy and after a few weeks presented a writhing, revolting sight. It was common practice for the men to keep their biscuit until nightfall, when they would attempt to eat it without being able to see exactly what they were chewing into. One admiral described the experience of eating ships' biscuit in the following terms: '...the biscuit was infested with numerous insects called weevils; they were bitter to the taste and a sure indication that the biscuit had lost its nutritious particles. These weevils soon grew into large maggots with black heads, these maggots were fat and cold to the taste, but not bitter.' The biscuit became so hard that no amount of soaking would soften it, and many fine examples can be seen in museums of what appear to be beautifully carved pieces of polished hard wood in the form of ships, miniature furniture, toys and dolls which are in fact made of nothing more than rock-hard ships' biscuit. The cheese does not seem to have been any better, as the men made buttons for their jackets and trousers with it, preferring its tough and durable quality to buttons made from common metal.

No matter how well provisioned a ship was at the outset of a voyage, scurvy could be expected to strike within a month. It is recorded that in 1780 six weeks after the Channel Fleet left port, 2,400 sufferers from scurvy were landed at Haslar Naval Hospital. Dr James Lind, the first superintendent of Haslar, reported the following facts at the beginning of the Seven Years' War in 1756: 'Altogether the number of seamen who died in time of war by shipwreck, capture, famine, fire or sword were inconsiderable in respect of such as are destroyed by ship diseases.' The figures he presented to substantiate his claim were: 133,708 men lost by disease, 1,512 died in action.

With the onset of scurvy, the men would become lethargic and listless, and minor tasks would prove exhausting. They took no interest in performing their duties, and in ignoring care for their safety many accidents and deaths resulted. Teeth would become loose in the gums and fall out. The gums would swell and putress. The legs would swell, articulated joints seize up and the skin become covered with dark and painful blotches. Men would fall down dead from the simple effort of rising to their feet or leaving their hammocks. And the cause? Lack of Vitamin C and to a lesser extent Vitamin D, which fresh fruit and vegetables would have supplied.

Dr James Lind, the aforementioned naval surgeon at Haslar, discovered the cause to be those vitamin deficiencies and recommended that naval ships carry fresh limes or alternatively lime juice as an effective antiscorbutic. Limes unfortunately had very little anti-scorbutic value compared with lemons. (The mistake arose because the West Indies called a lemon a lime.) One hundred and fifty years later vessels were still issuing lime juice, thinking it to be an effective antiscorbutic when they should have been issuing lemon juice. Since that time the Americans have always referred to British sailors as 'Lime-juicers', and 'Limeys' became their everyday vocabulary when referring to Englishmen generally.

Scurvy was not the only shipboard disease that seamen faced: yellow fever and malaria took a heavy toll in the mosquito-infested ports, while dysentery struck on the longer voyages as the bilges became more and more putrid with an accumulation of rubbish and sewage that settled in the loose stone or sand ballast deep in the hold. Most captains did not associate an insanitary ship with illness, and the word 'hygiene' had not been coined. To complete the record, rats had a free run of the ships, and cockroaches, lice, fleas and bed-bugs bred in profusion. It is not surprising that typhus spread rapidly through the packed messdecks with the virulence of the Black Death.

Victualling a ship was beset by two virtually insur-mountable problems – the impossibility of preserving food, especially in hot climates, and the avaricious peculation of the victualling contractors. For 200 years the ration scale on the King's Ships remained unchanged at one pound of salt pork or two pounds of salt beef on alternate days, one pound of biscuit and a gallon of flat beer, with a weekly issue of two pints of pease, three of oatmeal, eight ounces of butter and one pound of cheese. On tropical voyages a pint of wine or a half-pint of brandy replaced the hopeless flat beer, which would not keep and when sour caused virulent enteritis, rice took the place of oatmeal, and olive oil replaced butter. The cost of victualling was reckoned at 5 pence a man.

Such standards were not as they appeared, however. A ship's purser, the ship's 'man-of-business' and shop-keeper, handled all the stores of food, drink, tobacco and clothing. He received no regular pay, for he was regarded as a semi-civilian, but made his living by taking a commission on the goods he handled. He got five per cent on food and other comestibles and ten per cent on tobacco. He also worked on fourteen ounces to the pound, and the full measure of all other articles was reduced by one-eighth to compensate for wastage and seepage – this was known as 'the purser's eight'. The ship's books must always balance, even if it meant that the spirit ration was watered and the men were sold short.

Although officers wore regulation uniforms from 1748, the seamen did not do so until 1857. Until that time 'slops' (seamen's clothing) were provided by the purser out of his 'slop-chest', and with a complete monopoly he could charge virtually what he liked. As the seamen had no money until the ship completed her commission and then 'paid-off', the seamen had no recourse but to buy on credit – tick, they called it, from the 'tickets' issued by the purser upon whose redemption he also charged a handsome commission for the privilege of issuing credit. It is hardly surprising that the purser was the most hated man aboard a King's ship. There was a rhyme used by the sailors when the purser was in earshot, but out of sight, which showed what regard they had for his profession:

> Our b … of a purser, he is very handy.
> He mixes the water along with the brandy.
> The bloody old thief, he is very cruel:
> Instead of burgoo* he gives us water gruel.

> *burgoo – oatmeal porridge with meat added.

Pay was as low as the food was poor. At Trafalgar in 1805 a prime seaman received 19 shillings a month, a rate that had not risen since Samuel Pepys had been Secretary to the Navy Board in the reign of Charles II (1660-85). Soldiers at that period were paid a shilling a day, over twice as much.

Not only was pay low but the method of payment was unfair. To keep men on the ships and prevent them 'running' – deserting, there was no pay until the end of the voyage, when the ship 'paid off'. Then the men were issued with 'tickets' which could be cashed only at the Navy Offices in the port where the ship had started her commission, regardless of where the ship paid off. This resulted in men selling their tickets to publicans, tradesmen and money-lenders in the nearest port at robbery prices well below the full value of the tickets. The speculators then took all the tickets they had accumulated to the appropriate Navy Office and cashed them at their full value, to make a handsome profit.

These harsh conditions suffered by the seamen on the Lower Deck were in sharp contrast to the standard of living enjoyed by the officers. The officers' quarters, pay, allowances, prize money, rewards, food, drink, leave and work were all infinitely better. But there was no apparent class jealousy. In the mutinies of 1797 at Spithead and the Nore, a few officers were manhandled, and several were put ashore, but that was because they were bad officers, rather than just being officers. It is hard to credit the oppressed and often unwilling sailors possessing the qualities of moderation and loyalty toward their officer oppressors, yet that was the case, for the sailor had been born into a society which was sharply divided between rich and poor, privileged and unprivileged, and so the contrasts on board ship could be accepted.

These hardships were not the exception but the everyday lot which the Naval Tar accepted as part of his life. He was also subjected to a harsh discipline which would have him flogged for the slightest misdemeanour: speaking back to one of senior rank, being slow to respond to orders or hesitant in carrying out his duties. Death by hanging from the main yardarm automatically followed striking (feigned or imagined) of an officer, and death by 'flogging round the fleet' was a deserter's punishment. The deserter would be spreadeagled to a grating set in the ship's whaler, and he would be rowed to the gangway of each ship in the fleet and there, in front of each crew, he would be given one dozen lashes. With as many as thirty ships in each fleet, the man under punishment rarely survived. A humane captain might make a deserter's end a little less painful, although it would be just as final. The man would be hanged from his own ship's yardarm, with his messmates hauling him up to the main yardarm with a halter round his neck to choke out his life before the eyes of the crew as a warning to others.

But all this was purely secondary to the King's Navy's primary objective – that of fighting. The men would be expected to fight their ship against impossible odds and be victorious. The standing of the King's Navy at that time was such that it bred a contemptuous arrogance among the seamen and officers. The seamen of the day reckoned they and their ship could 'trounce 3 Frenchies and 5 Spaniards' – an exaggeration, of course, but records there are by the score that chronicle in matter-of-fact terms the actions of single, minor British ships of war arrogantly taking on, defeating and capturing any enemy who outgunned and outnumbered them numerically in ships and men.

This tradition was not lost with the passing of the era of Britain's 'wooden walls'. *Rawalpindi, Jarvis Bay, Glow-worm,* Narvik and Malta are just a few proud ships and places where sailors of this century emulated the fine traditions set in motion by their forefathers. Likewise the hard-won traditions of the merchant service are cherished by each successive generation, as shown by the indomitable spirit of the merchant sailor serving on the North Atlantic and Russian convoys during World War II.

In battle the seaman of the wooden-wall era would probably consider himself better off if killed outright, for to suffer the hell of the surgeon's knife in the candlelit cockpit – where probing, stitching and amputations were performed under rum-induced insensibility – was the terror of every man aboard. To survive such immediate horror usually led to an almost sure but painful and prolonged death, for without antiseptics gangrene would account for the deaths of ninety per cent of the wounded.

Casualties of battle, the stone-deaf from the roar of the guns, the blind, the disfigured, those with limbs missing and the stumps tarred, and those who had simply gone insane after what they had seen and endured, would find no gratitude or recompense from the Board of Admiralty, nor sympathy or benevolence from landsmen, but would be unceremoniously dumped ashore without pension and forgotten.

There was no Merchant Shipping Act until 1854, or active reformers like Samuel Plimsoll to fight for the rights of the Naval seamen, and it was only when they took matters into their own hands in 1797 in two desperate acts of despair and mutinied that they extracted a few basic rights in return for the majestic service they were rendering to their country.

In 1797 Britain was fighting for her life. She was at war with the three greatest sea-powers in Europe – France, the Netherlands and Spain. The French fleet was in Brest, ready to escort an invasion fleet to Britain, and the Dutch fleet was in the Texel estuary ready to help them by drawing off the British North Sea Fleet. At that moment Britain relied more than ever on the Home Fleet at Spithead and the North Sea Fleet at the Nore. On Easter Sunday the Home Fleet at Spithead mutinied and refused to put to sea. Pay was the main grievance.

The mutiny was a quiet, orderly and well-behaved affair, as can be seen from the letter sent from Valentine Joyce, the chief delegate on the Admiral's flagship *Queen Charlotte*, to all ships: 'Messmates … Proceed in your endeavours. Proceed in caution, peace and good behaviour. Let no disorder and tumult influence your proceedings … The greatest attention to be paid to the orders of the officers. Any person failing in respect due to them, or neglecting their duty, shall be severely punished ….' The men also gave the undertaking that the fleet would sail instantly if the French fleet came out of Brest, and they would not let British trade be damaged. It was a very gentlemanly mutiny in view of what they were trying to redress, and that gives a clear insight into the character of the professional sailor.

On St George's Day the mutiny was over. The Admiralty increased pay to 29s.6d. a week, and there were no reprisals. The seamen of the Home Fleet composed a ballad to commemorate the event:

The tars of old England have long toil'd in vain,
from the time of King Charles down to the present reign:
But their royal master their wages doth raise,
So join, British sailors, in King George's praise.
The fleet of Lord Bridport, the terror of France,
Petition'd the throne that their pay might advance.
Their petition was granted, each grievance redress'd,
In the heart of each seaman great George he is bless'd.

The Ballad of 1797

Hard on the heels of the Spithead mutiny, even though the demands had been met, the North Sea Fleet at the Nore mutinied. This was a different type of affair. Here the mutineers were not the true professional seamen but 'Quota' men. They blockaded the port of London, trade was stifled and food and fuel were soon in short supply. The Thames-side forts were fired upon, and officers manhandled and tarred and feathered. Soon the seamen loyal to the King and conscious of their country's plight deserted the mutineers, and the whole thing collapsed. No concessions were won, and the delegates' leader, Richard Parker, and twenty-nine others were hanged.

The repercussions from that affair did the seamen's cause no good. The fear which the landsman had felt at being left undefended in time of war now turned to hatred, and the profession of sailor was regarded with enmity.

Dr Johnson's views on the common sailor were: 'No man will be a sailor who has contrivance enough to get himself into jail; for being in a ship is being in jail, with the chance of being drowned. A man in a jail has more room, better food and commonly better company – what made anyone ever go to sea?' Where did the sailors come from willing to man the ships and endure such privations?

One could point to the 'press', of course. It is interesting to note that conscription is not a thing of the past: it took place as recently as the Korean War, with National Service, for it is still a nationally accepted contingency in time of war.

Once a man was 'pressed' and recorded on a ship's

muster book, he was in the King's service for life – or, more likely, until his untimely death. He was never allowed a run ashore for fear that he might desert. The ships never tied up alongside but anchored in mid-stream or way out in a roadstead, their wants being served by lighter and hoy. A guard-boat would circle an anchored ship day and night, with armed marines who were under orders to shoot any swimmers on sight.

To make life a little more bearable, many of the more humane captains allowed women on board while a ship was in a home port. Nelson's *Victory* hoisted a 'Wedding Garland' at the mast-head when she returned home, to show that wives and sweethearts were allowed on board.

Regulations were strict that all women should disembark before a ship sailed but the frailty of human affection often overruled the regulations. Women are known to have served as 'powder-monkeys' on many ships, and one even had a baby on board during the Battle of the Nile. One theory about the origin of the expression 'Show a leg' ('Get out of bed') is that the bosun's mate demanded to see a leg of those in hammocks before the ship sailed, to detect any women being taken on the voyage.

Even at the end of a ship's commission there was no liberty for the seamen. There was always an acute shortage of seasoned men to man ships awaiting to start a new commission, and the seamen would be transferred under armed guard to a waiting ship. The King's Navy was always short of hands – the mortality rate saw to that. Desertion was a hanging offence, and the only safe way a man could relieve himself of the service was for 'D.D.' to be entered alongside his name in the muster book – 'Discharged Dead'.

The press was never the sole means of filling the King's ships, however; volunteers were always forthcoming. Ships with illustrious names and captains renowned for their skill and daring in taking prizes advertised impending commissions in news broadsheets, and handbills were sent to principal towns. With dreams of rich rewards and daring escapades, prize money and fame, volunteers readily came forward.

Many volunteers came from the charity societies for orphans and abandoned boys. Just one of these, Hanway's Marine Society, provided 31,000 boys in the sixty years up to 1815. Others volunteered for the bounty, a lump sum varying from 30 shillings to £10, depending on the need for sailors and the generosity of the government at the time.

A further source of men, certainly not prime seamen though, and in many cases the most useless and resentful, awkward and dangerous to themselves and others, was the quota system. It was started by Act of Parliament during the war with France in 1795 because the press-gangs could not find enough seamen. Various counties and principal cities and even large towns had to produce given numbers of men to serve in the King's ships, their 'quota' of men. In the first quota Yorkshire had to provide 1,081 men, Lancashire 589, Devonshire 393, Dartmouth 394 and London 5,704, as just a few examples as the quota system spread nationwide.

The magistrates were delighted of the opportunity which the 'quota' provided to rid their regions of undesirables, and so a steady stream of criminals, rogues, vagabonds, smugglers, bankrupts, yokels and village simpletons was unleashed to serve in the King's ships. The 'quota men' did much to damage the name of the Navy, and the name 'sailor' became associated with all the aforesaid misfits. As the Nore mutiny was instigated by 'quota men', the reputation of the Navy in general and the sailor in particular had reached an all-time nadir.

Other men turned to the sea for very different reasons. Britain being an island, her seamen's traditions and skills are a national inheritance and develop anew with each new generation as long-cherished and proud ideals are emulated and surpassed. The British seaman has a simple make-up: his fortitude, constancy and valour in battle and his inherent belief in the greatness of his country and in the superiority of his own ship, his humour, self-reliance and constant ability to suffer privations and disease in order to further not too clearly understood ideals – these are the qualities which have manned British ships, merchant as well fighting ships, for well-over a thousand years.

Nelson recognized these qualities in the men serving under him and said of them: 'Aft the more honour; for'ard the better men.'

It was due in great measure to Nelson and the prestige of his great naval victories that hostility to the British seaman was reduced and his status was raised. To a nation newly delivered from the hands of a foreign tyrant, gratitude now knew no bounds. The Naval Tars were no longer regarded as social outcasts; overnight seemingly, they became admired as the chief defenders of Britain and her Empire. 'Rule Britannia' was broadsheeted across the length and breadth of the country, and broadside ballads glamorizing the life of the sailor and his victories were recounted with patriotic fervour wherever people met. No parlour was complete without a picture depicting Trafalgar, 'The Fall of Nelson' or even a portrait of Nelson suitably mounted in a black frame, and children, even the royal children, wore fashionable sailor-suits.

The promotion of national interest and appreciation generated a rise in the sailor's own self-respect, aided in no small measure by his becoming uniformed in 1857. The cessation of the quota system helped emphasize a new respectability. With the end of the war, impressment also ceased, pay was regularized and graded, and a career structure and pension structure were created. Excessive punishments and flogging ceased, and food improved; adequate shore leave became a right, and for the first time in a thousand years – since Alfred fought the Danes – the calling of sailor was respected enough to be acclaimed 'a worthy profession for any strong, sober and adventurous lad wishing to acquire the qualities of manhood'.

Whilst all this was happening in the King's Navy, similar improvements were occurring in the Merchant Marine, helped in part by the creation in 1859 of the Royal Naval Reserve which linked the two services, and by such reformers as Samuel Plimsoll, the insistence of A1 standards by Lloyds, and Trinity House's making landfall safer. Times were changing fast.

Our story of the sailing-ship sailor has run its course. The social, industrial and economic revolution was getting into its stride. Iron and steam were taking the place of wood and canvas, and the sailor was being replaced by the seaman. That was another era and another story, to be told no doubt by some future generation which will view today's technology with the same nostalgia as we regard the great age of sail. Who knows what developments await the merchant and fighting ships of the future? It is not inconceivable that the power of the wind and the forces of nature might not once again be used to direct ships about the oceans.

While we can prognosticate on the future and reflect on the past, it is sad to find that the merchant and fighting sailors of the past left so little of themselves behind when they had contributed so much to the writing of 'Great' in Great Britain. But their songs do remain, and perhaps by recalling them, and through them the men's hopes and aspirations, we can gain a brief insight of a very proud, brave race whose like we may never see again.

The following pages contain a legacy of haunting sea songs grouped together roughly as a sailor would sing them when going about his tasks. The number I have found has surprised me, and yet I know there must be many more. It does not need a trained voice to sing them, only enthusiasm, and they really do not need accompaniment. It needs only one to start off, and a cheerless night swinging to one's anchor at the beginning or end of a sailing season can be cheered and enlivened. Even the crustiest voice will mellow, and the most timid gather strength. They are still good morale-boosters and concerters of effort. Sing them. They really are grand songs. Abraham Cowley (1618-67), poet and essayist and a contemporary of Milton, wrote: 'Thou needest not make new songs but sing the old.'

# 3  Heaving Shanties

On sailing day the newly joined seaman would be roused from the forecastle by shouts and threats, and the laggardly would be assisted by a few cuffs and kicks to accelerate them in the right direction. The few experienced hands would no doubt be suffering thick heads, unsteady feet and 'jippy' stomachs after their last-night-before-sailing carousings. The rest of the crew would probably comprise landsmen, labourers and yokels who had been 'inspired' to go to sea by the broadside ballads, and those running from the law, vengeful husbands or jilted wives and spurned girl-friends. Their reason for being on board was of no importance; of more immediate concern was the speed in which they could be turned into prime seamen.

The windlass on the smaller and earlier ships, or the later capstan, would be the first piece of ship's mechanism they would encounter. The experienced hands would already have taken up the ash capstan bars and thrust them into the 'pigeon-holes' in the capstan head; the rest of the motley lot would be pushed into position by the mate to 'breast the bars'. The main capstan around which the men were now grouped would be connected by means of an endless rope 'messenger' to a smaller capstan some distance from it and positioned forward towards the bow.

The ship's boys, lads of around ten to twelve years, barefoot, ill-clothed, skinny and constantly hungry, would appear and take station alongside the anchor cable which would be running parallel to the messenger. As the men began heaving on the capstan bars and took a slow-measured tread, the boys would connect the messenger with hitches to the anchor cable by short lengths of rope known as 'nippers'. As the main capstan rotated (the smaller one was unmanned) the messenger would move between the two, pulling the nippers and the 'nipped' anchor cable inboard with it. As each nipper neared the main capstan, it would be 'fleeted' (released), and the boys would scamper forward again to repeat the process until the cable had been fully recovered. The lads employed in attaching the nippers were soon called 'nippers' themselves, and this gave birth to the word which nowadays denotes any small boy.

The capstan developed from the earlier windlass as ships and their gear grew bigger and heavier, eventually replacing it from about 1870 onwards. The larger capstans could take up to eight bars, with each bar taking up to six men, thus providing a primitive but none-the-less powerful machine which could haul a vessel of 300-400 tons deadweight against wind and tide and warp it in and out of the tightest dockside berth.

The capstan's predecessor, the horizontal barrel windlass, had itself evolved steadily over the years. The earliest spoke windlass, first recorded as being in use in the thirteenth century, also used removable hand-spikes resembling the capstan bars, but could harness the efforts of only one man either side and worked in short snatch-and-stop pulls as each bar had to be 'fleeted' as the barrel turned. In order to help the cable grip the barrel and also to prevent riding turn 'whelps', parallel chamferred wooden fillets were fitted around the barrel. This principle was also used on the later wooden capstans, subsequently to be cast as an integral part of the iron capstan.

The brake windlass – or 'jiggity-jig' windlass – which evolved about the middle of the nineteenth century was a big improvement, using a pull-you, push-you pumping action, with up to eight men working between the two bars. The pumping action transferred the effort to fixed gear-wheels operating either side of a ratchet. Pawls engaged the gear wheels with each upward stroke, thus rotating the barrel. As with its forerunner, this was a slow operation owing to its jerkiness.

Later still, with the development of iron-casting techniques, the rotary windlass became a familiar sight on the smaller coasting vessels, Northumberland collier brigs, Thames barges and Norfolk wherries and among the fishing fleets.

The development of the capstan at the expense of the windlass did not see its complete demise, and they were a common sight adjacent to mainmasts and the ships' holds, where they would still be used to aid the hoisting of spars and in loading and unloading cargo.

As the working techniques differed between capstan and windlass and even between different forms of windlass, so too did the shanties used to provide the correct working rhythms to suit each piece of machinery, although generally they were marching songs. Though the hauling would start with a brisk rhythm as the slack was taken in, the shantyman would change the tune to one of slower tempo for the actual 'heaving-in'.

Capstans were also frequently used for other forms of heaving. On square-rigged ships the bottom corners of the lowest and largest sails, the courses, were set and trimmed by means of ropes called 'tacks' and 'sheets'. As on today's modern 'fore-and-aft' yacht rig, the bottom corner of the sail closest to the wind was called the 'tack'; the rope attaching this to the deck was naturally known as the 'tack', the opposite corner being identified as the 'clew'; and the rope attached to the clew was known as the sheet. Going about and trimming sail necessitated hauling the enormous sail area and its corresponding heavy gear across and against the pressure of the wind, and the mechanical effort of the capstan would be used.

Windlass shanties were also frequently used for pumping ship, as there was a similarity in the 'jiggety-jig' action of both pieces of equipment.

# A-Roving

1. In Amsterdam there lived a maid.
    *Mark well what I do say.*
   In Amsterdam there lived a maid,
   And she was mistress of her trade.
   I'll go no more a-roving with you, fair maid.
    *A-roving, a-roving, since roving's been my ru-i-in,*
    *I'll go no more a-roving with you, fair maid.*

2. Her lips were red, her eyes were brown.
    *Mark well what I do say.*
   Her lips were red, her eyes were brown,
   And her hair was black and it hung right down,
   I'll go no more a-roving with you, fair maid.

3. I put my arm around her waist,
    *Mark well what I do say.*
   I put my arm around her waist,
   Cried she, 'Young man, you're in great haste.'
   I'll go no more a-roving with you, fair maid.

4. I took that maid upon my knee.
    *Mark well what I do say.*
   I took that maid upon my knee,
   Cried she, 'Young man, you're much too free.'
   I'll go no more a-roving with you, fair maid.

5. I kissed that maid and stole away.
     *Mark well what I do say.*
   I kissed that maid and stole away,
   She wept – 'Young man, why don't you stay?'
   I'll go no more a-roving with you, fair maid.

# Billy Boy

A fine example of Geordie dialect as used on the collier brigs.

1. Where hev ye been àál the day, Billy Boy, Billy Boy?
     *Where hev ye been àál the day, me Billy Boy?*
   I've been walkin' àál the day with me charmin' Nancy
   Grey.
     *And me Nancy kittled me fancy, Oh me charmin' Billy Boy.*

2. Is she fit ter by yer wife, Billy Boy, Billy Boy?
     *Is she fit ter be yer wife, me Billy Boy?*
   She's as fit ter be me wife as the fork is to the knife.
     *And me Nancy kittled me fancy, Oh me charmin' Billy Boy.*

3. Can she cook a bit o' steak, Billy Boy, Billy Boy?
     *Can she cook a bit o' steak, me Billy Boy?*
   She can cook a bit o' steak, aye, an' myek a gairdle cake,
     *And me Nancy kittled me fancy, Oh me charmin' Billy Boy.*

4. Can she myek an Irish stew, Billy Boy, Billy Boy?
     *Can she myek an Irish stew, me Billy Boy?*
   She can myek an Irish stew, aye, an' 'singin' hinnies' too.
     *And me Nancy kittled me fancy, Oh me charmin' Billy Boy.*

# The Black Ball Line

1. In the Black Ball Line I served my time.
     *Away-ay-ay, Horray-ah!*
   And that's the line where you can shine.
     *Hooraw for the Black Ball Line!*

2. The Black Ball ships are good and true.
   They are the ships for me and you.

3. They'll carry you along through frost and snow,
   And take you where the wind don't blow.

4. At Liverpool docks I bade adieu,

To Poll and Bet, and lovely Sue.

5. And now we're bound for New York Town.
   It's there we'll drink, and sorrow drown.

6. It's there I'll sport my long-tailed coat.
   It's there I'll sport my long-tailed coat.

## Can't You Dance the Polka?

1. As I walked down the Broadway,
   One ev'ning in July,
   I met a maid, she asked my trade,
   'A sailor lad,' sez I.
       *And away, yo' Santee,*
       *My dear Annie.*
       *Oh! You New York gals,*
       *Can't you dance the polka?*

2. To Tiffany's I took her.
   I didn't spare expense.
   I bought her two gold earrings,
   An' they cost me fifteen cents.

3. Said she, 'You lime-juice sailor,
   Now see me home you may.'
   But when at last we reached her door,
   Then to me she did say.

4. 'My flashman, he's a Yankee,
   With his hair cut short behind.
   He wears a pair of long sea-boots.
   He's a bos'n in the Blackball Line.

5. 'He's homeward bound this ev'ning,
   And alone with me will stay,
   So move along, you sailor lad,
   You had best be on your way.'

6. I kissed her hard and proper,
   Before her flashman came,
   Saying, 'Fare you well, you Bowery gel,
   I know your little game.'

7. I signed on a Yankee blood boat*,
   That sailed away next morn.
   Steer clear of all the Bowery gals,
   You're safer off Cape Horn.

*A ship renowned for the brutalizing of its crew.

# Clear the Track, Let the Bulgine Run

1. Oh! the smartest clipper you can find,
   *Ah ho way-ho, are you most done?*
   Is the Margret Evans o' the Blue Cross Line.
   *So clear the track, let the Bulgine run.*
   Tibby hey rig a jig in a jaunting car,
   *Ah ho way-ho, are you most done?*
   With Lizer Lee all on my knee,
   *So clear the track, let the Bulgine run.*

2. Oh! the Margret Evans of the Blue Cross Line,
   She's never a day behind her time.

3. Oh! when I come home across the sea,
   I'm goin' to marry Lizer Lee.

4. I thought I heard the old man say,
   'Just one more pull an' then belay.'

5. Oh! the gels are waitin' on the quay.
   It's the Margret Evans home from the sea.

6. Oh! now on shore we'll find our fun.
   Oh! fetch that gel with the red dress on.

7. Oh! the smartest clipper you can find
   Is the Margret Evans of the Blue Cross Line.

# Donkey Riding

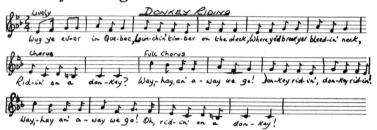

1. Wuz ye ever in Quebec,
    Launchin' timber on the deck,
    Where ye'd break yer bleedin' neck,
    *Ridin' on a donkey?*
        *Way, hay, an' away we go!*
        *Donkey ridin', donkey ridin'!*
        *Way, hay, an' away we go!*
        *Oh, ridin' on a donkey!*

2. Wuz ye ever in Timbuktoo,
    Where the gals are black an' blue,
    Where they waggle their bustles at you,
    *Ridin' on a donkey?*

3. Wuz ye ever in Vallipo,
    Where them gals put on a show,
    Waggle an' wriggle wid a roll 'n' go,
    *Ridin' on a donkey?*

4. Wuz ye ever down Mobile Bay,
    Screwin' cotton all the day,
    A dollar an' a half is a white man's pay,
    *Ridin' on a donkey?*

5. Wuz ye ever in Canton,
    Where the men wear pigtails long,
    An' the gals play hong-ki-kong,
    *Ridin' on a donkey?*

6. Wuz ye ever in London town,
    Where them gals they do come down,
    To see a king in a golden crown,
    *Ridin' on a donkey?*

7. Wuz ye ever in Mirramashee,
   Where ye tie up to a tree,
   An' the skeeters do bite we,
   *Ridin' on a donkey?*

8. Wuz ye ever in Broomielow,
   Where them Yanks is all the go,
   An' the gals dance heel an' toe,
   *Ridin' on a donkey?*

9. Wuz ye ever down 'Frisco Bay,
   Where the gals all shout 'Hooray!
   Here comes Johnny wid 'is three years' pay,
   *Ridin' on a donkey'?*

10. Wuz ye ever off Cape Horn,
    Where yer backside's never warm,
    When yiz wish ter hell ye'd niver bin born,
    *Ridin' on a donkey?*

It is reputed that this shanty had over a hundred verses, as each new port and experience found in it would itself put to verse.

## The Drummer and the Cook

1. Oh there was a little drummer and he loved a one-eyed
   cook,
   And he loved her, oh he loved her, though she had a
   cock-eyed look.
       *With her one eye in the pot,*
       *And the other up the chimney,*
       *With a Bow-wow-wow,*
       *Fal-lal the dow-a-did-dy,*
       *Bow-wow-wow.*

2. When this couple went a-courtin' for to walk along the
   shore,
   Sez the drummer to the cookie, 'You're the gel that I
   adore.'

3. When this couple went a-courtin' for to walk along the
   pier,
   Sez the cookie to the drummer, 'An' I love you too, my
   dear.'

4. Sez the drummer to the cookie, 'Ain't the weather fine
   today?'
   Sez the cookie to the drummer, 'Is that all ye got to say?'

5. Sez the drummer to the cookie, 'Will I buy the weddin'
   ring?'
   Sez the cookie, 'Now yer talkin'. That would be the very
   thing.'

6. Sez the drummer to the cookie, 'Will yer name the
   weddin' day?'

Sez the cookie, 'We'll be married in the merry month o'
May.'

7. When they went to the church to say 'I will', the
   drummer got a nark*,
   For her one eye gliffed** the parson, an' the other killed
   the clerk.

*nark: a disagreeable surprise caused by a person, not by circumstance
**gliff: to frighten

## Hog's-Eye Man

1. Oh the hog's-eye man is the man for me.
   He were raised way down in Tennessee.
   Oh hog's eye, oh!
   *Row the boat ashore for the hog's eye.*
   *Steady on a jig with a hog's-eye, Oh!*
   *She wants the hog's-eye man.*

2. Oh who's been here while I've been gone?
   Some big buck nigger with his sea-boots on?
   Oh hog's-eye, oh!

3. Oh bring me down my riding cane,
   For I'm off to see my darling Jane.
   Oh hog's-eye, oh!

4. Oh a hog's-eye ship, an' a hog's-eye crew,
   An' a hog's-eye mate and a skipper too.
   Oh hog's-eye, oh!

# Hullabaloobalay

1. My father kept a boardin' house.
   *Hullabaloobalay,*
   *Hullabaloobalaybalay.*
   The boardin' house was on the quay.
   *Hullabaloobalay.*

2. The boardin' house was on the quay.
   The lodgers were nearly all at sea.

3. A flash young feller called Shallow Brown,
   Followed me mother all round the town.

4. Me father said, 'Young man, me boy,'
   To which he quickly made reply.

5. Next day when Dad was in the Crown,
   Me Ma ran off with Shallow Brown.

6. Me father slowly pined away,
   When me Ma came back on the following day.

# Johnny Come Down to Hilo

1. I nebber see de like since I bin born,
   When a big buck nigger wid de sea-boots on
   *Says, 'Johnny come down to Hilo.*
   *Poor old man.'*
   *Oh wake her, oh shake her.*

*Oh wake dat gel wid de blue dress on,*
*When Johnny comes down to Hilo,*
*Poor old man.*

2.  I lub a liddle gel across de sea.
    She's a Badian* beauty an she sez to me.

3.  Oh was yo nebber down Mobile Bay
    A screwin' cotton all de day?

4.  Did ye ebber see de ol' plantation boss
    An' de long-tailed filly and de big black hoss?

5.  I nebber seen de like since I bin born,
    When a big buck nigger wid de sea-boots on.

*Badian – short for Barbadian, a native of Barbados.

# Leave Her Johnny

1.  I thought I heard the Old Man say,
      *'Leave her, Johnny, leave her;*
    You may go ashore and draw your pay',
      *And it's time for us to leave her.*

2. You can make her fast and pack your gear,
   You can have her moored 'longside the pier,

3. The winds were foul, the trip was long,
   And before we leave we'll sing a song,

4. We'll sing, oh may we never be,
   On a hungry ship the likes of she,

5. The food was bad, the wages low,
   And now ashore again we'll go,

6. The bunks were hard and the watches long,
   The seas were high and the winds were strong,

7. She'd neither stay, nor steer, nor wear,
   She shipped it green and she made us swear,

8. Her sails are stowed and our work is done,
   So now on shore we'll find our fun.

# Liverpool Judies

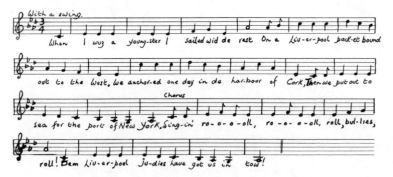

1. When I wuz a youngster I sailed wid de rest,
   On a Liverpool packet bound out to the West.
   We anchored one day in de harbour of Cork,
   Then put out to sea for the port of New York.
   *Singin' ro-o-o-oll, ro-o-o-oll, roll, bullies, roll!*
   *Dem Liverpool judies have got us in tow!*

2. For forty-two days we wuz hungry an' sore.
   Oh the winds wuz agin us, the gales they did roar;
   Off Battery Point we did anchor at last,
   Wid our jib-boom hove in an' the canvas all fast.

3. De boardin'-house masters wuz off in a trice,
   A-shoutin' an' promisin' all that wuz nice;
   An' one fat ol' crimp he got cotton'd to me,
   Sez he, 'Yer a fool, lad, ter follow the sea.'

4. Sez he, 'There's a job as is waitin' fer yer,
   Wid lashin's o' liquor an' beggar-all to do';
   Sez he, 'What d'yer say, lad, will ye jump 'er too?'
   Sez I, 'Ye ol' bastard, I'm damned if I do.'

5. But de best ov intentions dey niver gits far,
   After forty-two days at the door of a bar;
   I tossed off me liquor an' what d'yer think?
   Why the lousy ol' bastard 'ad drugs in me drink.

6. Now, the next I remembers I woke in de morn
   On a three-skys'l yarder bound south round Cape Horn;
   Wid an' ol' suit o' oilskins an' three pairs o' sox,
   An' a bloomin' big head an' a dose o' the pox.

7. Now all ye young sailors take a warnin' by me,
   Keep a watch on yer drinks when the liquor is free;
   An' pay no attintion to runner or whore,
   Or yer head'll be thick an' yer fid'll be sore.

# The Liverpool Packet

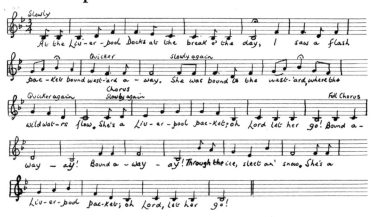

1. At the Liverpool Docks at the break o' the day,
   I saw a flash packet bound west'ard away.
   She was bound to the west'ard, where the wild waters
     flow.
   *She's a Liverpool packet; oh Lord, let 'er go!*
     *Bound away! Bound away!*
     *Through the ice, sleet an' snow.*
     *She's a Liverpool packet;*
     *Oh Lord, let 'er go!*

2. Oh, the time o' her sailin' is now drawin' nigh,
   Stand by all ye lubbers we'll wish ye goodbye;
   A pair o' clean heels to ye now we will show.
   *She's a Liverpool packet; oh Lord, let 'er go!*

3. An' now we are leavin' the sweet Salthouse Dock.
   All the boys an' the gals on the pierhead do flock;
   All the boys an' the gals are all shoutin' hurro!
   *She's a Liverpool packet; oh Lord, let 'er go!*

4. An' now we are waitin' in the Mersey so free,
   Awaitin' the tugboat to tow us to sea;
   An' we'll round the Rock Light where the salt tides do
     flow.
   *She's a Liverpool packet; oh Lord, let 'er go!*

5. Sheet home yer big tops'l, haul aft yer jib sheets,
   Sheet home fore'n aft, boys, ye'll git no darn sleep;
   Come aft now, God damn yers, come aft, make a show.
   *She's a Liverpool packet; oh Lord, let 'er go!*

6. An' now we are howlin' down the wild Irish sea,
   Our passengers are merry an' their hearts full o' glee,
   Our sailors like tigers they walk to an' fro.
   *She's a Liverpool packet; oh Lord, let 'er go!*

7. An' now we are sailin' the Atlantic so wide,
   An' the hands are now ordered to scrub the ship's side;
   Now then, holystones, boyos, the bosun do blow.
   *She's a Liverpool packet; oh Lord, let 'er go!*

8. An' now we are off of the Banks o' Newf'n'land,
   Where the bottom's all fishes an' fine yeller sand;
   An' the fishes they sing as they swim to an' fro.

*She's a Liverpool packet; oh Lord, let 'er go!*

9. An' now we're arrivin' in ol' New York town;
   We're bound for the Bowery, an' let sorrow drown;
   With our gals an' our beer, boys, oh, let the song flow.
   *She's a Liverpool packet; oh Lord, let 'er go!*

# Lowlands

1. I dreamed a dream the other night,
       *Lowlands, my Lowlands. Hurray my Jo.*
   I dreamed I saw my own true love,
       *Lowlands, my Lowlands away.*

2. I dreamed my love came in my sleep,
   And quoth 'My dear, why do you
       weep?'

3. He was wet and clothed with weed so
       cold,
       'I shall never kiss you again,' said he.

4. 'I'm drown'd in the Lowland sea,' he
       said,
       'And wet green weed is now my bed.'

5. Oh, my love is drown'd in the far-off
       seas,
       And never more shall I him please.

6. I will cut my bonny hair,
       No other man shall think me fair.

7. No other man shall joy with me,
       I will cut my breasts until they bleed.

# One More Day

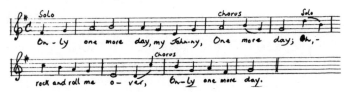

1. Only one more day, my Johnny,
   *One more day;*
   Oh, rock and roll me over,
   *Only one more day.*

2. Don't you hear the Old Man howling?

3. Don't you hear the mate a-growling?

4. No more gales or heavy weather.

5. Only one more day together.

6. Can't yer hear them gals a-calling?

7. Pack your bag today, my Johnny.

# Rio Grande

1. Now were you ever in Rio Grande?
   *Away-ay Rio!*
   It's there that the river runs down golden sand,
   And we're bound for the Rio Grande.
   *Then away, Rio away,*
   *Away down Rio.*
   *So fare you well, my bonny young girl,*
   *And we're bound for the Rio Grande!*

2. The oak, and the ash and the bonny birk tree.
   *Away-ay Rio!*
   They're all growing green in the North Countrie.
   And we're bound for the Rio Grande.

3. Where are you steering for, my pretty maid?
   *Away-ay Rio!*
   And have you a sweetheart, my pretty maid?
   And we're bound for the Rio Grande.

4. May I stay with you, my pretty maid?
   *Away-ay Rio!*
   'I'm afraid you're a bad one, kind sir,' she replied,
   And we're bound for the Rio Grande.

5. So it's pack up your sea-chest and get under way.
   *Away-ay Rio!*

The gels we are leaving will all get our pay,
And we're bound for the Rio Grande.

6. Sing good-bye to Sally, and good-bye to Sue,
     *Away-ay Rio!*
   And you who are listening, good-bye to you.
   For we're bound for the Rio Grande.

7. Now fill up yer glasses, and say fare ye well,
     *Away-ay Rio!*
   To the pretty young lasses who loved us too well.
   For we're bound for the Rio Grande.

8. Good-bye, fare ye well, all you gels of the town,
     *Away-ay Rio!*
   And when we come back, you may get a new gown,
   For we're bound for the Rio Grande.

9. Our ship went a sailing out over the bar,
     *Away-ay Rio!*
   And we pointed her nose for the Southern Star,
   For we're bound for the Rio Grande.

10. Farewell and adieu to you ladies of Spain,
      *Away-ay Rio.*
    And we're all of us coming to see you again,
    For we're bound for the Rio Grande.

11. I said 'Farewell' to Kitty, my dear,
      *Away-ay Rio.*
    And she waved her white hand as we passed the south
      pier,
    And we're bound for the Rio Grande.

12. We've a jolly good ship and a jolly good crew.
      *Away-ay Rio.*
    We've jolly good mates, and a good skipper too,
    And we're off to the Rio Grande.

# Sacramento

1. As I went a strolling down the quay,
   *Hoodah to me hoodah,*
   A trim young craft I chanced to see,
   *Hoodah, doodah day.*
   *Blow, boys, blow for Californio,*
   *There's plenty of gold, so I've been told,*
   *On the banks of the Sacramento.*

2. Her hair was black, her eyes were blue,
   Her lips were red, and were good to view,

3. I doffed my cap and sez, 'How do!'
   She tacks and sez, 'Quite well, thank you!'

4. I asked her then to come with me,
   Down to the docks my ship to see.

5. She swiftly answered, 'Oh dear, no.
   I thanks you but I dare not go.'

6. 'I have a sweetheart brave and true,
   So cannot give my love to you.'

7. And so I bade this craft adieu,
   I said that gals like her were few.

# Sally Brown

1. Oh, Sally Brown of Boston city.
     *Way-hay-ay, roll and go;*
   Sally Brown, you're very pretty.
     *Spend my money on Sally Brown.*

2. For Sally Brown she's a bright mulatto,
   She drinks rum and chaws terbaccer.

3. My Sally Brown's a Creole lady,
   I guess she's got a nigger baby.

4. Seven long years I courted Sally,
   Said she, 'My boy, why do you dally?'

5. But Sally Brown's a white man's daughter.
   She sent me sailing 'cross the water.

6. So Sally Brown, I will not grieve you,
   Sally Brown, I'll not deceive you.

# Santiana*

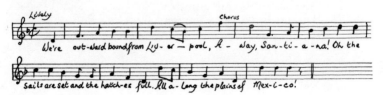

1. We're outward bound from Liverpool,
     *Away, Santiana!*
   Oh the sails are set and the hatches full,
     *All along the plains of Mexico!*

2. We're outward bound for Mexico,
   To Mexico where the whalefish blow.

3. In Mexico where the land lies low,
   Where there ain't no snow, an' the whalefish blow.

4. In Mexico so I've heard say,
   There's many a charmin' señorita gay.

5. Them gals is fine with their long, black hair.
   They'll rob yer blind an' skin yer bare.

6. Them Spanish gals I do adore.
   They all drink vino an' ax' for more.

7. In Mexico I long to be,
   Wid a tight-waisted gal all on me knee.

8. Why do them yellar gals love me so?
   Because I don't tell 'em all I know.

9. When I wuz a young man in me prime,
   I'd chase them little gals two at a time.

10. But now I'm old an' getting grey,
    Rum's me sweetheart every day.

11. Santiana gained his name,
    At Molly del Rey** he gained his fame.

12. An' General Taylor ran away,
    An' Santiana gained the day.

13. 'Twas on the field at Molly del Rey,
    Santiana lost a leg that day.

14. So heave her up an' away we'll go,
    All along the plains of Mexico!

*The name by which the sailors knew General Antonio Lopez de Santa
Anna, the last President of Mexico before the annexation of Texas,

California and New Mexico by the United States of America.
**The sailor's corruption of 'Molina del Rey', where a
famous battle took place in 1847.

# Shenandoah

1. Missouri, she's a mighty river.
   *Away, you rolling river.*
   The Indian camp lies on her border.
   *And away, I'm bound away,*
   *'Cross the wide Missouri.*

2. O, Shenandoah! I love your daughter.
   I'll take her 'cross the rolling water.

3. The Chief refused the white man's offer,
   And vowed the white man should not have her.

4. One day a ship sailed up the river,
   And brought the Chief the strong fire-water.

5. With Yankee notions she was laden,
   Her Captain loved the Indian maiden.

6. He made the Chief drunk with fire-water,

And 'cross the river stole the daughter.

7. O, Shenandoah! I long to hear you.
   Across the wide and rolling river.

# Valparaiso Round the Horn

'Twas a cold an' drea-ry mor-nin' in De-cem-ber (De-cem-ber) An' all of me
mon-ey it wuz spent (it wuz spent), Where it went to, Lord, I can't re-mem-ber (re-
*Chorus*
mem-ber) So down to the ship-pin' of-fice went (went, went) Pad-dy lay back!
Paddy lay back! Take in yer slack. Take in yer slack. Take a turn a-
(*Shouted*)
round yer cap-stan, heave a pawl, heave a pawl! — 'Bout ship sta-tions boys be handy, be han - dy! For we're bound for Val-la-pa-rais-er round the Horn!

1. 'Twas a cold an' dreary mornin' in December
   (December),
   An' all of me money it wuz spent (it wuz spent),
   Where it went to, Lord, I can't remember (remember),
   So down to the shippin' office went (went,went).
   *Paddy, lay back! Paddy, lay back!*
   *Take in yer slack! Take in yer slack!*
   *Take a turn around yer capstan, heave a pawl, heave a pawl!*
   *'Bout ship stations boys be handy, be handy!*
   *For we're bound for Vallaparaiser round the Horn!*

2. That day there wuz a great demand for sailors (for
   sailors),
   For the colonies and for 'Frisco and for France (an' for
   France),
   So I shipped aboard a Limey called the Hotspur (the
   Hotspur),
   An' got paralytic drunk on my advance ('vance, 'vance).

3. Now I joined 'er on a cold December mornin'.
   A-frappin o' me flippers to keep me warm,
   With the south cone a-hoisted as a warnin',
   To stand by the comin' of a storm.

4. Now some of our fellers had been drinkin',
   An' meself wuz heavy on the booze;
   An' I sat upon me ol' sea-chest a-thinkin',
   I'd turn in my bunk an' have a snooze.

5. I woke up in the morning' sick an' sore,
   An' knew I wuz outward bound again;
   When I heard a voice a-bawlin' at the door,
   'Lay aft, men, an' answer to yer names!'

6. 'Twas on the quarterdeck where I first saw 'em.
   Such an ugly bunch I'd niver seen before;
   For there wuz a bum an' stiff from every quarter,
   An' it made me poor ol' heart feel sick an' sore.

7. There wuz Spaniards an' Dutchmen an' Rooshians,
   An' John Crapoos just across from France;
   An' most of 'em couldn't speak a word o' English,
   But answered to the name of 'Month's Advance'.

8. I wisht I wuz in the Jolly Sailor,
   Along wid Irish Kate a-drinkin' beer;
   An' then I thought what jolly chaps were sailors,
   An' with me flipper I wiped away a tear.

9. I knew that in me box I had a bottle,
   By the boardin'-master 'twas put there;
   An' I wanted something for to wet me throttle,
   Somethin' for to drive away dull care.

10. So down upon me knees I went like thunder,
    Put me hand into the bottom of the box;
    An' what wuz my great surprise an' wonder,
    Found only a bottle of medicine for the pox.

# We're All Bound To Go

1. Oh Johnny was a rover,
   And today he sails away.
   *Heave away, my Johnny,*
   *Heave away-ay.*
   Oh Johnny was a rover,
   And today he sails away.
   *Heave away, my bully boys,*
   *We're all bound to go.*

2. As I was walking out one day,
   Down by the Albert dock,
   I heard an emigrant Irish girl
   A-talkin' with Tapscott.

3. 'Good mornin', Mister Tapscott, sir.'
   'Good mornin', my gel,' sez he.
   'It's have you got a packet ship
   That's bound for Amerikee?'

4.  'Oh yes, I've got a packet ship,
    I have got one or two.
    I've got the Jenny Walker
    An' I've got the Kangaroo.'

5.  'I've got the Jenny Walker
    And today she does set sail,
    'With five an' fifty emigrants
    And a thousand bags o' male.*'

6.  Bad luck to thim Irish sailor lads,
    Bad luck to thim, I say,
    For they all got drunk an' broke into me bunk
    An' stole me clothes away.

*male: the Irish pronunciation of meal.

# What Shall We Do with the Drunken Sailor?

1. What shall we do with the drunken sailor?
   What shall we do with the drunken sailor?
   What shall we do with the drunken sailor
   Early in the morning?
   > *Hooray and up she rises,*
   > *Hooray and up she rises,*
   > *Hooray and up she rises*
   > *Early in the morning.*

2. Put him in the long-boat until he's sober
   Early in the morning.

3. Pull out the bung and wet him all over
   Early in the morning.

4. Put him in the scuppers with the deck pump on him
   Early in the morning.

5. Heave him by the leg in a running bowlin'
   Early in the morning.

6. Tie him to the taffrail when she's yard-arm under
   Early in the morning.

# The Wild Goose Shanty

1. I'm the Shanty-man of the Wild Goose Nation.
   *Tibby way-ay, hioha!*
   I've left my wife on a big plantation.
   *Hilo my Ranzo Hay!*

2. Now a long farewell to the old plantation.
   Now a long farewell to the old plantation.

3. Oh the boys and the gels went a huckleberry hunting.
   Oh the boys and the gels went a huckleberry hunting.

4. Then good-bye and farewell you rolling river.
   Then good-bye and farewell you rolling river.

5. And a long farewell to the Wild Goose Nation.
   And a long farewell to the Wild Goose Nation.

6. I'm the Shanty-man of the Wild Goose Nation.
   I've left my wife on a big plantation.

# 4 Hauling Shanties

## Halyards – Long-haulers

A Long Time Ago
Blood-Red Roses
Blow, My Bully Boys, Blow!
Blow the Man Down
Boney was a Warrior
Cheerly Man
Dead Horse
Good Morning, Ladies All
Hanging Johnny
Haul Away, Joe
John Kanaka
Lizer Lee
Poor Old Joe
Reuben Ranzo
Roll the Cotton Down
Roll the Old Chariot
Sailor Likes His Bottle, O!, The
Sing Fare You Well
Stormalong
Tommy's Gone to Hilo
Whisky Johnny

## Tacks and Sheets – Short-haulers

Haul upon the Bowline
Johnny Boker
Oh, Come Roll Him Over
Roll and Go
Sailors Three
We'll Haul the Bowlin'

Hauling shanties are quite unlike those used for capstan work which accompanied protracted and continuous exertion – retrieving the bower anchor could easily occupy half an hour's heaving at the bars. The hauling shanties differed in both length and tempo, for generally halyard work involved vigorous activity of short duration.

Halyard hauling shanties were usually of two types: those required for 'long hauling' and those to accompany the 'sweating-up' of halyards or 'bowsing-down' of tacks and clews.

The ships of the period were square-riggers, and 'long hauling' at the halyards was necessary to hoist the yards for setting sail, while a short, strong pull was needed to haul the sheets and braces taut when constantly trimming the sails to the wind.

A square-rigged, three-masted ship would identify her masts from forward as being the foremast, mainmast and mizzenmast. Each mast comprised three parts: the lower mast, the top mast and the topgallant mast. The sails were attached to the masts by wooden yards which crossed the masts at right angles – hence the generic term 'square-rigger'.

Depending upon the size of the ship, each mast might accommodate up to six square sails, two to each section. Each sail would be identified precisely by preceding it by the mast to which it was set: fore-upper top sail, main lower topgallant etc. A number of fore-and-aft sails such as the flying jib, outer jib, inner jib, jib, forestaysail and a number of other similar triangular sails set between the masts would also comprise the ship's sail wardrobe.

Certain sails were set by being hauled up the masts by their yards (for example, the upper topsails and upper topgallants), while for vessels carrying royals, the royal yards were carried in the half-raised position, the yards being fully raised and the sails being dropped to their working position. The main sails or main courses, the lower topsails and the lower topgallant sails were attached to fixed yards and simply released to hang down.

To set the main sails or main courses, the lower topsails and the lower topgallant sails being attached to fixed yards, the topmen (sail-handlers) made their way out along the yards, released the lines, securing them to the yards (the gaskets), and allowed the sails to fall. While the topmen were scrambling aloft, the deck seamen were busy releasing the clewlines by which, when furling the sail, they had hauled up the lower corners of the sail to the yard, also the buntlines by which they had hauled up the centre of the sail. With the sails released and hanging free, they would then be trimmed to the wind by hauling on the sheets. With the wind filling the sail, this would be a very heavy task. Only the 'short-pull' shanties would accompany the sail-trimming, and such ballads as 'Johnny Boker', 'Haul upon the Bowline', 'Blow, Boys, Blow' and 'Reuben Ranzo' would be used where the short refrain would end with the men shouting the action words, usually two to each chorus, and exerting concerted pulls at the same time.

The upper topsails and the upper topgallant sails necessitated the massive yards being moved up and down the masts, and long-hauling shanties concerted this effort. In order to reconcile the weight to be moved by the manpower available, the blocks on the tackle would have four or more sheaves, thus necessitating a very long pull to overhaul all the parts of the rope, and such long shanties as 'Whisky Johnny', 'Blow the Man Down' and 'Drunken Sailor' would be used. Much of this type of hauling would be regarded as 'stamp-and-go', the seamen tailing onto the fall and walking away with it, with men constantly leaving the end of the rope to run forward again to take up another pull.

Halyard shanties also accompanied other tasks. In the tropics the ultra-violet rays of the intense sunlight rotted sails and rapidly weakened the stitching, and it was common practice for ships to bare their yards and stow the sails below decks until time for sailing. The sails would be rolled up and made into long sausage-shaped rolls while still on the yards, then sent down for stowing. Gantlines would be rigged to hoist the sails aloft again, and the halyard shanties would be sung to unify the effort.

Another common task would be undertaken when a ship

entered or left the quieter latitudes of the tropics. Heavy-weather gear and sails would be taken off or refurled for the expected stronger winds of the northern hemisphere, and again the hauling would be accompanied by the singing of halyard shanties.

When a square-rigger tacked through the wind in order to go about, the angle of the sails was altered by moving the yards. These were controlled by wire braces attached to the ends of each yard. On the command of 'Going about', the crew would tail onto the windward braces and run along the deck, hauling as they went, singing the hauling shanties known as 'stamp-and-goers'.

The fore-and-aft sails (forestay sail, jibs) were set on stays running down from the foremast to a spar sticking forward beyond the ship's bow to a bowsprit, if made of one section, or a jib-boom, if more than one piece. These staysails and jibs were hoisted hand-over-hand to the time of the short-haul shanties.

It will be appreciated from the above explanations that hauling shanties, unlike capstan songs, comprised a wide variety, differing in length, varied in tempo and used for a variety of purposes. Some, such as the long-haul songs, are pleasantly melodious, while those of the short-pull variety accompanying the sweating-up of sheets and tacks were not much more than wild shouts.

## Halyards – Long-haulers

## A Long Time Ago

1. A long, long time and a very long time,
   *To me way-ay-ay-ah.*
   A long, long time and a very long time,
   *A long time ago.*

2. Away down South where I wuz born,
   Among the fields of golden corn,

3. A Yankee packet lay out in the bay,
   A-waitin' a fair wind to get under way,

4. There once wuz a family lived on a hill,
   An' if they're not dead they're all livin' there still,

# Blood-Red Roses

1. Me bonnie bunch o' roses O!
   *Hang down, ye blood-red roses, hang down!*

'Tis time for us to roll 'n' go!
*Hang down, ye blood-red roses, hang down!*
Ooh! ye pinks 'n' posies!
*Hang down, ye blood-red roses, hang down!*
Ooh! ye pinks 'n' posies!
*Hang down, ye blood-red roses, hang down!*

2. We're bound out to Iquique Bay.
   We're bound away at the break of day.

3. We're bound away around Cape Horn.
   We wisht ter 'ell we'd niver bin born.

4. Around Cape Horn we all must go,
   Around Cape Stiff through the ice an' snow.

5. Me boots an' clothes are all in pawn,
   An' it's bleedin' draughty around Cape Horn.

6. 'Tis growl ye may but go ye must.
   If ye growl too hard, yer head they'll bust.

7. The gals are waitin' right ahead.
   A long strong pull should shift the dead.

8. Them Spanish whores are pullin' strong.
   Hang down, me boys, it won't take long.

9. 'Oh, rock an' shake 'er' is the cry.
   The bloody topm'st sheave is dry.

10. Just one more pull an' that'll do.
    We're the buckos fer ter kick 'er through.

# Blow, My Bully Boys, Blow!

mast and yards were all a qui-ver. Blow me bull-y boys, blow! Her blow!

1. Say, wuz ye niver down the Congo River?
   *Blow, boys, blow!*
   Ooh! yes, I've bin down the Congo River,
   *Blow, me bully boys, blow!*

2. Congo she's a mighty river,
   Where the fever makes the white man shiver.

3. A Yankee ship came down the river.
   Her masts an' yards were all a quiver.

4. How d'yer know she's a Yankee clipper?
   By the blood an' guts that flow from her scuppers.

5. How d'yer know she's a Yankee liner?
   By the stars an' bars that fly behind her.

6. How d'yer know she's a Yankee packet?
   She fired her guns an' I heard the racket.

7. Who d'yer think's the skipper of her?
   A bow-legged bastard from the Bowery.

8. Who d'yer think's the chief mate of her?
   Why Hog's-Eye Bill, that big buck nigger.

9. What d'yer think we 'ad fer breakfast?
   Nice new chains an' a helping of the whiplash.

10. What d'yer think we 'ad fer dinner?
    Belayin' pin soup an' a squeeze thro' the wringer.

11. What d'yer think we 'ad fer supper?
    The starboard side of an' old Sou'wester.

12. What d'yer think we 'ad fer cargo?
    Black sheep breaking the Embargo.

13. Blow terday, an' blow termorrer,
    Blow fer this hell ship o' sorrer.

# Blow The Man Down

## Version 1

1. Oh, as I wuz a-rollin' down Paradise Street,
   *Timme way, hay, blow the man down!*
   A fat Irish bobby I chanc't for to meet.
   *Ooh! gimme some time to blow the man down!*

2. Sez he, 'Yer a Blackballer by the cut o' yer hair,
   An' the long red-topped seaboots that I see you wear!

3. 'Ye've sailed in some packet that flies the Blackball.
   Ye've robbed some poor Dutchman of boots, clothes an'
   all.'

4. 'O mister, O mister, ye do me great wrong.
   I'm a flying-fish sailor just home from Hong Kong.'

5. So I spat in his face, an' stove in his jaw,
   Sez he, 'Young fellar, yer breakin' the law!'

6. They gave me six months, boys, in Liverpool town,
   For bootin' an' kickin' an' blowin' him down.

7. Now all ye young fellars what follows the sea,
   ' Put yer vents to the wind an' jus' lissen to me.

8. I'll give ye a warnin' afore we belay,
   Steer clear o' fat policemen – ye'll find it'll pay.

9. Wid a blow the man up, bullies, blow the man down,
   An' a crew of hard cases from Liverpool Town.

# Version 2

1. Oh blow the man down, bullies, blow the man down,
       *To me way-ay, blow the man down.*
   Oh blow the man down, bullies, blow him away,
       *Oh gimme some time to blow the man down.*

2. We went over the bar on the 13th of May,
   The Galloper jumped, and the gale came away.

3. Oh the rags they wuz gone, and the chains they wuz
   jammed,
   An' the skipper sez he, 'Let the weather be hanged.'

4. As I was a-walkin' down Winchester Street,
   A saucy young damsel I 'appened to meet.

5. I sez to her, 'Polly, and how d'you do?'
   Sez she, 'None the better for seein' of you.'

6. Oh, it's sailors is tinkers, and tailors is men,
   An' we're all of us coming to see you again.

7. So we'll blow the man up, an' we'll blow the man down,
   An' we'll blow him away into Liverpool Town.

# Version 3

1. O blow the man down, bullies, blow the man down!
       *Way-hay, blow the man down.*
   O blow him right back into Liverpool Town!
       *O! give us some time to blow the man down.*

2. Come listen to me an' I'll sing yez a song,
Of the thing that befell me new home from Hong Kong.

3. As I wuz strolling down Paradise Street,
A pretty young maiden I chanced for to meet,

4. This pretty young maiden she said unto me,
'There's a fine full-rigged clipper just ready for sea.'

5. So I packed up my sea-chest and signed on that day,
An' with that sweet maiden I spent all my pay.

6. The fine full-rigged clipper for Sydney was bound.
She wuz very well-manned and very well-found.

7. As soon as that clipper was clear of the bar,
Her mate knocked me down with the end of a spar.

8. Her skipper was pacing the break of the poop,
And he helped me on with the toe of his boot.

9. As soon as that clipper had got out to sea,
I'd cruel hard treatment of every degree.

10. So all you young fellows who follow the sea,
Give me yez attention, jus' listen ter me.

11. Don't you go a-strolling down Paradise Street,
Or just such a chowlat you'll chanc't for to meet.

12. An' I'll give yez fair warnin', afore we belay,
Don't ever take heed of what pretty gals say!

# Boney Was a Warrior

1. Boney was a warrior,
   *Way-ay yah.*
   Boney was a warrior,
   *John France-wah.* *

2. Boney beat the Rooshuns,
   Boney beat the Rooshuns,

3. Boney beat the Prooshuns,
   Boney beat the Prooshuns.

4. Boney went to Moscow,
   Boney went to Moscow,

5. Moscow was a-fire,
   Moscow was a-fire,

6. Boney he came back again,
   Boney he came back again,

7. Boney went to Elbow**
   Boney went to Elbow,

8. Boney went to Waterloo,
   Boney went to Waterloo,

9. Boney was defeated,
   Boney was defeated,

10. Boney was a prisoner,
    'Board the 'Billy Ruffian'***

*'France-wah': sailors' pronunciation of 'François'.
**Elbow: Elba.
***'Billy Ruffian': sailors' affectionate name for the ship-of-the-line *Bellerophon*, which conveyed Bonaparte into exile.

11. Boney was sent away,
    'Way to Saint Helena-ay.

12. Boney broke his heart and died,
    Boney broke his heart and died,

13. Boney was a warrior.
    *Way-ay yah.*
    Boney was a warrior.
    *Way-ay yah.*

# Cheerly Man

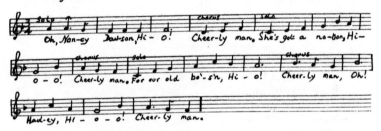

1. Oh, Nancy Dawson, Hi-o!
       *Cheerly man.*
   She's got a notion, Hi-o-o!
       *Cheerly man.*
   For our old bo's'n, Hi-o!
       *Cheerly man, Oh!*
       *Hauley, Hi-o-o!*
       *Cheerly man.*

2. Oh, Betsey Baker, Hi-o!
   Lives in Long Acre, Hi-o-o!
   Married a Quaker, Hi-o!

3. Oh, Sally Rackett, Hi-o!
   Pawned my best jacket, Hi-o-o!
   Then sold the ticket, Hi-o!

4. Oh, fighting cocks, Hi-o!
   Oh, bust the blocks, Hi-o-o!
   Oh, stretch her luff, Hi-o!

5. Oh, Sally Rackett, Hi-o!
   Is a beginner, Hi-o-o!
   Prefers it to her dinner, Hi-o!

# Dead Horse

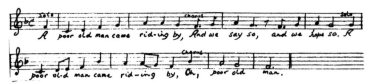

1. A poor old man came riding by,
      *And we say so, and we hope so.*
   A poor old man came riding by,
      *Oh, poor old man.*

2. Avast, old man, your horse will die,

3. He's carted stones for many a year,

4. An' if he lives, why, he I'll ride,

5. An' if he dies, I'll tan his hide,

6. An' salt him down for sailor's use,

7. Dead horse, dead horse, what brought you here?

This rendition closely resembles 'Poor Old Joe'. (p.96).

# Good Morning, Ladies All

1. Now a long good-bye to you, my dear,
    *With a heave-oh haul.*
   And a last farewell, and a long farewell,
    *And good morning, ladies all.*

2. For we're outward bound to New York town,
   And you'll wave to us till the sun goes down.

3. And when we're back again in London Docks,
   All the pretty girls will come in flocks.

4. And Poll and Jane and Sue will say.
   'Oh, here comes Johnny with his three years' pay.'

5. So a long good-bye to you, my dear,
   And a last farewell, and a long farewell.

# Hanging Johnny

1. Oh they call me Hanging Johnny.
   *Away, boys, away.*
   They says I hang for money.
   *Oh hang, boys, hang.*

2. And first I hanged my daddy,
   And first I hanged my daddy.

3. And then I hanged my mother,
   My sister and my brother.

4. And then I hanged my granny,
   And then I hanged my granny.

5. And then I hanged my Annie,
   I hanged her up say canny.*

6. We'll hang and haul together,
   We'll haul for better weather.

*'Say canny' is the Northumbrian term for 'so carefully'.

# Haul Away Joe

1. Way, haul away, we'll haul away the bowline.
    *Way, haul away, haul away, Joe.*
   Way, haul away, the packet is a-rollin'.
    *Way, haul away, haul away, Joe.*

2. Oh when I was a little boy, my mother always told me,
   That if I didn't kiss the girls, my lips would all go
   mouldy.

3. Oh once I had a nigger gal, an' she wuz fat an' lazy,
   An' next I had a Spanish gal, she nearly drove me crazy.

4. King Louis wuz the King o' France afore the Revolution,
   But then they did cut off his head an' spoiled his
   constitution.

5. Oh once I had a scoldin' wife, an' she wuz far from civil.
   I clapped a plaster on her mouth an' sent her to the
   Devil.

6. So, way, haul away, we'll haul for better weather.
   Way, haul away, we'll hang an' haul together.

# John Kanaka

1. I heard, I heard the Old Man say,
    *John Kanaka-naka-tulai-e!*
   Today, today is a holiday.
    *John Kanaka-naka-tulai-e!*
   Tulai-e, ooh! tulai-e!
    *John Kanaka-naka-tulai-e!*

2. We'll work termorrer, but no work terday.
   We'll work termorrer, but no work terday.

3. We're bound away for 'Frisco Bay.
   We're bound away at the break o' day.

4. We're bound away around Cape Horn.
   We wish ter Christ we'd niver bin born.

5. A Yankee ship wid a Yankee crew.
   Oh, we're the buckos fer ter kick 'er through.

6. A Yankee ship wid a Yankee mate.
   If yer stop ter walk, he'll change yer gait.

7. Oh, haul away! Oh, haul away!
   Oh, haul away, an' make yer pay!

# Lizer Lee

1. Lizer Lee, she promised me.
     *Yankee John, Stormalong.*
   She promised for to marry me.
     *Yankee John, Stormalong.*

2. Oh Lizer Lee, she slighted me.
   Now she will not marry me.

3. When I sailed across the sea,
   Lizer said she'd be true to me.

4. I promised her a golden ring.
   I promised her a golden ring.

5. Up aloft this yard must go.
   Mister Mate he told us so.

6. I thought I heard the skipper say,
   'One more pull an' then belay.'

# Poor Old Joe

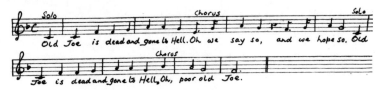

1. Old Joe is dead and gone to Hell.
     *Oh, we say so, and we hope so.*
   Old Joe is dead and gone to Hell.
     *Oh, poor old Joe.*

2. He's as dead as a rat on the store-room floor.

3. He won't come hazing us no more.

4. The ship did run, the waves did roar.

5. He's as dead as a nail in old Chippy's store.

This shanty could be 'stretched' for the duration of any task by the shantyman's improvising the many and varied ways in which Old Joe could be 'as dead as …'.

# Reuben Ranzo

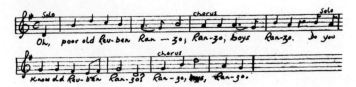

1. Oh, poor old Reuben Ranzo;
    *Ranzo, boys, Ranzo.*
   Do you know old Reuben Ranzo?
    *Ranzo, boys, Ranzo.*

2. Oh, Ranzo was no sailor;
   Old Ranzo was a tailor;

3. So he shipped aboard a whaler;
   Aboard a Glo'ster whaler;

4. But he could not do his duty;
   But he could not do his duty;

5. Old Ranzo couldn't steer her;
   Old Ranzo wouldn't steer her;

6. D'ye hear anything queerer?
   D'ye hear anything queerer?

7. Oh, Ranzo washed each fortnight;
   Oh, Ranzo washed each fortnight;

8. He said it was his birthright;
   He said it was his birthright;

9. They triced up this man so dirty;
   They triced up this man so dirty;

10. And gave him six and thirty;
    And gave him six and thirty;

11. But the Cap'n had a daughter;
    But the Cap'n had a daughter;

12. Cried, 'Father, do have mercy!'
    Cried, 'Father, do have mercy!'

13. She took him to her cabin;
    She took him to her cabin;

14. And gave him cake and brandy;
    And gave him cake and brandy;

15. She gave him education;
    She gave him education;

16. And taught him navigation;
    And taught him navigation;

17. And now he's Capt'n Ranzo;
    And now he's Capt'n Ranzo;

18. And capt'n of that whaler;
    And capt'n of that whaler;

# Roll the Cotton Down

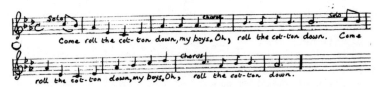

1. Come roll the cotton down, my boys.
   *Oh, roll the cotton down.*
   Come roll the cotton down, my boys.
   *Oh, roll the cotton down.*

2. Away down south where I wuz born.

3. Come all you little nigger boys.

4. A dollar a day is a black man's pay.

5. A dollar-and-a-half is a white man's pay.

6. The black man's pay is rather low.

7. The white man's pay is rather high.

8. If de sun don't shine, dem hens won't lay.

9. Oh, around Cape Horn we're bound to go.

10. So hoist that yard and start a song.

11.  Oh, stretch it aft and sing this song.

# Roll the Old Chariot

1.  Oh, a drop of Nelson's blood wouldn't do us any harm.
    Oh, a drop of Nelson's blood wouldn't do us any harm.
    Oh, a drop of Nelson's blood wouldn't do us any harm,
      *An' we'll all hang on behind!*
      *So we'll ro-o-oll the old chariot along!*
      *An' we'll roll the golden chariot along!*
      *Oh, we'll ro-o-oll the old chariot along!*
      *An' we'll all hang on behind!*

2.  Oh, a plate of Irish stew wouldn't do us any harm.

3.  Oh, a nice fat cook wouldn't do us any harm.

4.  Oh, a roll in the clover wouldn't do us any harm.

5.  Oh, a long spell in gaol wouldn't do us any harm.

6.  Oh, a nice watch below wouldn't do us any harm.

7.  Oh, a night with the gals wouldn't do us any harm.

8.  Oh, a job on a farm wouldn't do us any harm.

# The Sailor Likes His Bottle, O!

1. So early in the morning,
   The sailor likes his bottle, O.
   A bottle o' rum and a bottle o' gin
   And a bottle of Irish whiskey, O!
     *So early in the morning,*
     *The sailor likes his bottle O!*

2. So early in the morning,
   The sailor likes his 'baccy, O.
   A packet o' shag and a packet o' twist
   And a packet o' Yankee Doodle, O!
     *So early in the morning,*
     *The sailor likes his 'baccy, O!*

3. So early in the morning,
   The sailor likes the lassies, O.
   The lassies o' Blyth, and the lassies o' Shields,
   And the lassies across the water, O!

*So early in the morning,*
*The sailor likes his lassies, O!*

# Sing Fare You Well

1. Fare you well, I wish you well.
   *Hooraw and fare you well.*
   Fare you well till I return.
   *Hooraw, sing fare you well.*

2. Oh, fare you well, my bonny young gel.
   Oh, fare you well, my bonny young gel.

3. As I walked out one morning fair,
   It's there I met a lady fair.

4. At her I winked, I do declare.
   At her I winked, I do declare.

5. Up aloft this yard must go.
   Up aloft this yard must go.

6. I thought I heard the skipper say,
   'One more pull an' then belay.'

7.  Fare you well, I wish you well.
    Fare you well till I return.

# Stormalong

1.  Oh Stormy's gone that good old man.
    *Stormyalong, boys, Stormalong John.*
    Oh Stormy he is dead and gone.
    *Ay, ay, ay, Mister Stormalong.*

2.  Oh Stormy he is dead and gone.

3.  We dug his grave with a silver spade.

4.  We lowered him down with a golden chain.

5.  We carried him away to Mobile Bay.

6.  We'll never see his like again.

7.  Stormy was a good old man.

8.  Stormy he is dead and gone.

# Tommy's Gone to Hilo

1. Tommy's gone and I'll go too,
   *Away down Hilo.*
   Oh, Tommy's gone, and I'll go too.
   *Tom's gone to Hilo.*

2. Tommy's gone to Mobile Bay,
   Oh, Tommy's gone to Mobile Bay.

3. Tommy's gone to Trafalgar,
   Oh, Tommy's gone to Trafalgar.

4. The Old Victory led the way,
   The brave old Victory led the way.

5. Tommy's gone for evermore,
   Oh, Tommy's gone for evermore.

6. He didn't kiss his lass good-bye,
   It broke her heart and made her cry.

# Whisky Johnny

1. Oh whisky is the life of man,
   *Whisky Johnny.*
   Oh whisky is the life of man,
   *Whisky for my Johnny.*

2. Oh whisky makes me pawn my clothes,
   And whisky gave me this red nose.

3. Oh I had a daughter, name of Sue,
   She'll drink her tot an' yours too.

4. Oh whisky killed my poor old dad,
   An' whisky drove me mother mad.

5. If the Mersey wuz whisky an' I were a duck,
   I'd dive right in an' sup it all up.

6. Oh, it's whisky up an' whisky down,
   An' whisky all around the town.

7. Oh, whisky here, an' whisky there,
   Oh, I'll have whisky anywhere.

8. Oh, whisky is the life of man,
   An' I'll sup it from an old tin can.

# Haul upon the Bowline

1. Haul upon the bowline, the fore and maintop bowline.
   *Haul upon the bowline, the bowline, HAUL!* [Shouted]

2. Haul upon the bowline, the fore-t'ga'nt bowline.

3. Haul upon the bowline, the main-t'ga'nt bowline.

4. [A variety of bowlines can be named, depending upon the type of ship and task in hand.]

5. Haul upon the bowline, so early in the morning.

6. Haul upon the bowline; the ship she be a-sailing.

7. Haul upon the bowline; the ship she be a-rolling.

8. Haul upon the bowline; 'Frisco's* a fine town.

9. Haul upon the bowline; my Judie lives in 'Frisco.

10. Haul upon the bowline; and Judie is me darlin'.

11. [Here Judie's many vices and virtues would be extolled.]

12. Haul upon the bowline; the waves they are a-breakin'.

13. Haul upon the bowline; the mate he's always a-growlin'.

14. Haul upon the bowline; the Old Man is a-cursing.

15. Haul upon the bowline; it's a long way to pay-day.

*Or any other port.

## Johnny Boker

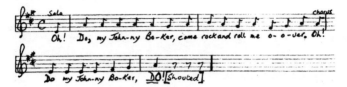

1. Oh! Do, my Johnny Boker, come rock and roll me over.
   *Oh! Do, my Johnny Boker, DO!* [Shouted]
   Oh! Do, my Johnny Boker, come rock and roll me over.
   *Oh! Do, my Johnny Boker, DO!* [Shouted]

2. Oh! Do, my Johnny Boker. The Old Man ain't no sailor.

3. Oh! Do, my Johnny Boker. The mate, he's niver sober.

4. Oh! Do, my Johnny Boker. The bos'n wuz a tailor.

5. Oh! Do, my Johnny Boker. Cook's an undertaker.

The sailors would ad-lib throughout the ship's company and after-guard.

## Oh, Come Roll Him Over

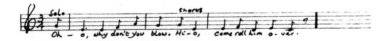

1. Oho, why don't you blow.
   *Hio, come roll him over.*

2. One man – to strike the bell.

3. Two men – to man the wheel.

4. Three men – t'gallant braces.

5. Four men – to heave the lead.

6. Five men – to grease the truck.

7. Six men – to dip the well.

8. Seven men – to pump her dry.

9. Eight men – to man the yard.

10. Nine men – to knot and splice.

11. Ten men – to dip the ensign.

…ad infinitum.

## Roll and Go

1. There was a ship, she sailed for Spain.
   *Oh-o-o, roll and go.*
   There was a ship and she sailed for Spain.
   *Oh-o-o, roll and go.*

2. There was a ship came home again.

3. What d'ye think she had in her hold?

4. There wuz nutmegs, and there wuz gold.

5. An' what wuz in her lazaret?

6. Rotting split peas and bad hoss meat.

Many more verses would be sung, each sailor giving the benefit of his own inspiration.

# Sailors Three

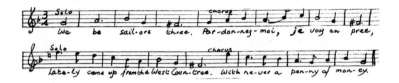

1.  We be sailors three.
    *Pardonnez-moi, je vous an pree,*\*
    Lately come up from the West Countree.
    *With never a penny of money.*

2.  Here, good fellow, I drinks to thee,
    And to all good fellows, whoever they be,

3.  And he who will not pledge me this,
    Pray for the shot, whatever it is,

4.  Charge it again, lad, charge it again,
    As long as ever there's ink in the pen,

\*'Pardonnez-moi, je vous emprie': Forgive me, please.'

# We'll Haul the Bowlin'

1.  We'll haul the bowlin' so early in the morning.
    *We'll haul the bowlin', the bowlin' HAUL!* [Shouted]

2.  We'll haul the bowlin', for Kitty is my darlin'.

3. We'll haul the bowlin', for fore-top-gallant bowlin'.

4. We'll haul the bowlin'; the skipper is a-growlin'.

5. We'll haul the bowlin'; the packet is a-rollin'.

6. We'll haul the bowlin'; so early in the mornin'.

This shanty lends itself to the virtuosity of the shantyman and to the type and rig of the vessel.

# 5   Pumping Shanties

Fire Down Below
Packet Ship, The
Paddy Doyle's Boots
Strike the Bell
Yaw, Yaw, Yaw

The old wooden square-riggers, working in all weathers and always sailed hard to save a tide or win a freight, with no opportunity for underwater attention or careenage, constantly worked their seams and consequently leaked badly as soon as they cleared the shelter of the land. The sea also made its way below decks through flexing deck seams and butt ends, down the hatchways and any deck access in heavy weather to add to the accumulation already swirling about in the bilges.

Pumping the water over the side again was a very strenuous and miserable task, using the 'jiggety-jig' pump. In the northern latitudes and in any lively seaway it was common for the men to spend watch and watch, day in, day out, heaving up and down on the rocker bars simply to keep the ship afloat.

The output of the pumps was very low compared with the energy expended, as they were situated at deck-level and needed to raise the water from the bilges at least forty feet below by sucking it up leaky leather tubes, whose suction was provided by sliding hollow leather-clad wooden cylinders with leather non-return flap valves up and down the tubes, whose connecting rods were operated by pump handles on the deck.

The rhythm of the pumping shanties was jerky and well suited to the short pulling-and-pushing motion of the task, as 'Stormalong', 'Lowlands' and 'Fare-ye-Well' well illustrate.

The old 'jiggety-jig' pump was eventually replaced by the rotary Downton pump needing only two men to each of the flywheel handles. The suction tubes and the cylinders were more efficient, but still the work was back-breaking, and long periods were still spent pumping ship. For prolonged pumping more men could be put to the pumps by attaching 'bell-ropes' to the flywheel handles, one leading forward and one aft. Men would tail onto these ropes, each team adding weight or giving way at the critical moment to bring the flywheel round and keep it moving vigorously. The back-aching and exhausting task of bending and lifting was much reduced, and while the efficiency of the pump itself was appreciably an improvement over the 'jiggety-jig' pump, it could also be worked for longer periods.

Real pumping shanties were few in number, as the short-haul shanties were ideally suited to that task.

## Fire Down Below

1. Fire in the galley, fire down below.
   It's fetch a bucket of water, girls,
   There's fire down below.
       *Fire, fire, fire down below.*
       *It's fetch a bucket of water, girls,*
       *There's fire down below.*

2. Fire in the fore-top, fire in the main.
   It's fetch a bucket of water, girls,
   And put it out again.

3. Fire in the chart-room, fire in the crow.
   It's fetch a bucket of water, girls,
   There's a fire down below.

4. Fire in the fore-peak, fire down below.
   It's fetch a bucket of water, girls,
   There's fire down below.

5. Fire in the windlass, fire in the chain.
   It's fetch a bucket of water, girls,
   And put it out again.

6. Fire in the jib-boom, fire in the bow.
   It's fetch a bucket of water, girls,
   There's fire down below.

7. Fire in the futtocks, fire in the drain.
   It's fetch a bucket of water, girls,
   And put it out again.

8. Fire up aloft, and fire down below.
   It's fetch a bucket of water, girls,
   There's fire down below.

# The Packet Ship

1. Bounty was a packet ship,
       *Pump ship, packet ship!*
   Sailing on a cruising trip,
       *In the South Pacific!*

2. Billy Blight*, that silly man,
   Was the master in command.

3. He was growling day and night,
   Whether he was wrong or right.

4. On the Bounty there were rules,
   Not for soft an' silly fools.

5. An' the answer for complaints.
   Handcuffs an' the iron chains.

6. Spittin' on the quarterdeck,
   Punishment – a broken neck.

7. There was troubles every day;
   Many sailors ran away.

8. An' at last that Billy Blight
   With his crew commenced to fight.

9. Brawlin', kickin' everywhere,
   Iron pins flew through the air.

10. Mates and sailors in the night
    Overpowered Billy Blight.

11. They put Billy Blight afloat,
    With his madness, in a boat.

12. Bounty then went out of sight;
    Left alone was Billy Blight.

13. Billy Blight he reached the coast,
    But the Bounty she was lost.

14. Many gales have crossed the sea,
    Since the Bounty went away.

15. Never was there heard a word,
    From the crew that stayed on board.

*Captain William Bligh (1763-1817) true rank lieutenant but called captain as courtesy title for anyone commanding a ship. Served under Captain Cook. As a result of his experiences in the South Seas given command of the *Bounty* with instructions to collect bread fruit plants to transport to the West Indies and the southern states of America to set up plantations to feed the slaves. Crew mutinied at Tahiti after alleged harsh treatment and set Bligh adrift with eighteen men in an open boat. They survived and most reached England. The leader of the mutineers, Fletcher Christian, after many troubles, led the survivors of the mutiny to set up a colony on an uninhabited island now known as Pitcairn Island.

# Paddy Doyle's Boots

1. To my way-ay-ay-ah,
   We'll pay Paddy Doyle for his boots.

2. To my way-ay-ay-ah,
   We'll all throw dirt at the cook.

3. To my way-ay-ay-ah,
   We'll all drink brandy and gin.

# Strike the Bell

1. Aft on the poop deck, walkin' about,
   There is the second mate, so steady an' so stout.
   What he is thinkin' of, he doesn't know himsel'.
   Oh, we wish that he would hurry up an' strike, strike
   the bell.

*Strike the bell, second mate! Let us go below.*
*Look well to wind'ard, ye can see it's gonna blow.*
*Look at the glass, ye will see it has fell,*
*An' we wish that you would hurry up an' strike, strike the*
*bell!*

2. Down on the maindeck workin' at the pumps,
   There is the larboard watch a-longin' for their bunks;
   Lookin' to wind'ard they see a great swell,
   They're wishin' that the second mate would strike, strike
   the bell.

3. Aft at the wheel poor Anderson stands,
   Grasping at the spokes wid his cold, mittened hands;
   Lookin' at the compass, oh, the course is clear as hell,
   He's wishin' that the second mate would strike, strike
   the bell.

4. For'ard on the forecastle-head keeping sharp lookout,
   There is 'Lampy' standin', ready for to shout,
   'Lights burnin' bright, sir, an' everything is well!'
   He's wishin' that the second mate would strike, strike
   the bell.

5. Aft on the quarterdeck our gallant capt'n stands,
   Lookin' to wind'ard his glasses in his hands.
   What he is thinkin' of, we know very well,
   He's thinkin' more of shortening sail than strike, strike
   the bell!

# Yaw, Yaw, Yaw!

1. Mein vader vos ein Dutchman,
   Mit mein yaw, yaw, yaw!

Mein vader vos ein Dutchman.
*Mit mein yaw, yaw, yaw!*
Mein vader vos ein Dutchman
Und mein mutter vos ein Prussian,
*Mit mein yaw, yaw, yaw!*

2. Und I spoke ein hotch-potch lingo,
Und I spoke ein hotch-potch lingo,
Und I spoke ein hotch-potch lingo,
Gott for Dommey und O by Yingo!

3. Mit mein niggerum, buggerum, stinkum,
Mit mein niggerum, buggerum, stinkum.
Vell, ve'll climb upon der steeples,
Und ve'll spit down on der peoples!

4. Und der polisman, fireman, steepleman,
Und der polisman, fireman, steepleman,
Dey all climb upon der steeple,
Und dey laugh do all der peoples.

5. Oh, ven I vos ein sailor,
Oh, ven I vos ein sailor,
Vell ve drink up all der visky,
Und it makes us feel damn frisky.

6. Ve did all de bawdy houses,
Ve did all de bawdy houses,
Und ve hitchum up der trousers,
Und ve catchem all der louses.

7. Ve chase all der bretty fräuleins,
Ve chase all der bretty fräuleins,
Und ve chase um, und ve tease um,
Und ve catch em, and ve kees um.

# 6   Forebitters

According to the Act
Alabama, The
Banks of Newfoundland, The
Bosun's Alphabet, The
Ebenezer, The
Fire Ship, The
Flying Cloud, The
Gals Around Cape Horn, The
Goodbye, Fare-ye-Well
High Barbaree
Leave 'er, Johnny, Leave 'er
Paddy West
Ratcliffe Highway
Rolling Home
Rondo for Sledging
Sailor's Way, The
Salt Beef
Saucy Arabella, The
Spanish Ladies
Stately Southerner, The
Whale, The

Not all Sailor Jack's songs were shanties. Many, those called forebitters, were not work-songs but were sung for pleasure when the men relaxed during the second dog-watch.

A sailor's working day was quite different from that of the landsman. He worked split shifts of four hours, called a watch, with four hours rest off watch. Such a division of the twenty-four hour period would give an unfair division, with the hours of darkness always falling to the same men. In order to ensure that the men shared the day and night watches evenly, the 4 p.m. to 8 p.m. watch was divided into two: the first dog-watch, 4 p.m. to 6 p.m., during which the men would perform light duties and eat, and the second dog-watch, 6 p.m. to 8 p.m., their only period of relaxation, in which they would wash and mend clothing, whittle models from pieces of wood or bone (scrimshaw work), sing songs and make their own entertainment. Work and sleep occupied the other watches.

The watch-keeping system on board ship is as follows:

| | |
|---|---|
| Midnight to 4 a.m. | – Middle watch |
| 4 a.m. to 8 a.m. | – Morning watch |
| 8 a.m. to noon | – Forenoon watch |
| Noon to 4 p.m. | – Afternoon watch |
| 4 p.m. to 6 p.m. | – First dog-watch |
| 6 p.m. to 8 p.m. | – Second dog-watch |
| 8 p.m. to midnight | – First watch |

In the cold northern latitudes or in heavy weather, the men would gather together and take their relaxation below decks in the forecastle, battening themselves in to contain what little warmth they could generate. On mild nights or in the tropics, this ritual would take place on deck in the open air around the forebitts, where the men would gather to smoke or 'chaw terbaccy', yarn and inevitably sing, and so the location of their singing gave its name to the songs – forebitters.

When relaxing, it was natural that Sailor Jack's thoughts should turn away from shipboard topics and stray to memories of home, family and loved ones, drinking and the delights of shoreside preoccupations. His singing reflected this and ranged from the bawdy to the melancholy – it is rare to find a forebitter which does not describe his longing to be on shore and away from the sea and ships.

A great many sea-songs written in the late 1700s and early 1800s were believed by the public at large to be sea- or sailor-inspired. The songs described deeds of daring, gales and wrecking, the joy of working a ship of sail and the comradeship in doing so, and they generously extolled the honourable profession of seamen. In truth, most of these songs were little more than 'chapbooks' (pamphleted ballads bearing a slight resemblance to broadside ballads; (see p.150) which had never known salt water and were written in great numbers by the hack ballad-writers of the day to be sold by chapmen (street vendors) to an impressionable public far removed from the sea. These 'slipsongs' (artificially sentimental and without substance) were never heard sung around the forebitts but were good music-hall entertainment for landsmen after a few drinks on Saturday night.

The manner of detecting a genuine forebitter from a chapbook or slipsong is in the content. The sailor did not sentimentalize about the sea and its hardships; he sang of the land and things associated with it, whereas the latter romanticized the sea and sailors while being well detached from them.

## According to the Act*

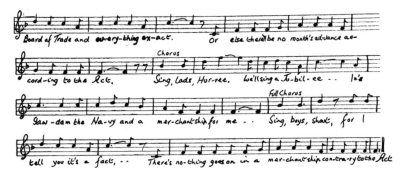

1. If you want to join a British ship, you must not roam at
   large.
   If you want to join a British ship, you must have a good
   discharge.
   It must be signed by the Board of Trade and everything
   exact,
   Or else there'll be no month's advance according to the
   Act.
   > *Sing, lads, hurree. We'll sing a Jubilee.*
   > *It's Gaw-dam the Navy and a merchant ship for me.*
   > *Sing, boys, shout, for I tell you it's a fact,*
   > *There's nothing goes on in a merchant ship contrary to the*
   > *Act.*

2. Now when you sign the articles, you have to hear them
   read.
   They tell you of your pork and beef, your water an' yer
   bread,
   Yer coffee, tea an' butter, an' everything exact,
   Yer lime juice and yer vinegar – according to the Act.

3. An' when you get aboard, my lads, yer heads feel rather
   sore.
   You expect to get good watch and watch, like you have
   had before.
   But the mate bawls out, 'Lay aft, all hands! Jus' do as I
   direct!'
   For 'watch and watch' the first day out's contrary to the
   Act.

4. Haul away the weather mainbrace and ease away the
   lee;

Hoist jib and tops'ls and let the sheets go free;
Lay aft with a luff tackle; heave down the lee main tack;
For I'm goin' to have this main-course set according to
the Act.

5. So aft along the decks, my lads, with many a curse we go,
Wishin' that eight good bells would strike an' we could
go below.
Eight bells is struck, the watch lays aft, the log is hove
exact.
Then – relieve the wheel and go below – according to the
Act.

*The Merchant Shipping Act, 1876; see p.28.

# The Alabama

1. When the Alabama's keel was laid,
   *Roll, Alabama, roll,*
   It was laid in the yard of Jonathan Laird.
   *Oh, roll, Alabama, roll.*

2. It was laid in the yard of Jonathan Laird.
   It was laid in the town of Birkenhead.

3. Down the Mersey Ways she sailed out then,
   And Liverpool fitted her with guns and men.

4. To the Southern States she then sailed forth,
   To destroy the commerce of the North.

5. Into Cherbourg port she sailed one day,
   For to take her share of prize money.

6. Many sailor lads they met their doom,
   When a cruising frigate appeared in view.

7. And a ball from the frigate fired that day,
   Shot the Alabama's stern away.

8. Off the three-mile limit in '65,
   The Alabama went to her grave.

*Alabama.* A vessel, regarded as a fighting frigate, built in Birkenhead (Jonathan Laird's Yard) for the Confederate States of America in the American Civil War. Her offensive cruising caused great devastation to the North's economy and a great loss of shipping. According to a court of arbitration the British Government of the day had to pay to the newly established United States Government heavy damages amounting to £3 million.

# The Banks of Newfoundland

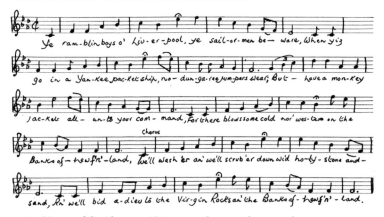

1. Ye ramblin' boys o' Liverpool, ye sailormen beware,
   When yiz go in a Yankee packet ship, no dungaree jumpers wear;
   But have a monkey jacket all unto yer command,
   For there blows some cold nor'westers on the Banks of Newf'n'land.

   *We'll wash 'er an' we'll scrub 'er down wid holystone an' sand,*

An' we'll bid adieu to the Virgin Rocks an' the Banks of
Newf'n'land.

2. We had on Lynch from Ballynahinch, Spud Murphy and
   Moike Moore,
   'Twas in the winter of seventy-three them sea-boys
   suffered sore;
   They popped their clothes in Liverpool, some sold them
   all out o' hand,
   Not thinking of them cold nor' winds on the Banks of
   Newf'n'land.

3. We had a lady passenger – Bridget Reilly wuz her name,
   To her I promised – on me she had a claim;
   She tore up her red flannel drawers, me boys, to make
   mittens for our hands,
   For she could not see them sea-boys freeze, on the Banks
   of Newf'n'land.

4. I dreamt a dream the other night, an' t'ought I wuz home,
   I dreamt that me and my judie wuz back in Marry-bone;*
   We both wuz in the ale-house, wid a jug o' ale in hand,
   Then I awoke an' found no joke, on the Banks o'
   Newf'n'land.

5. The mate comes up on the fo'c'slehead an' loudly he
   does roar,
   'Rattle 'er in, me lively lads. We're off Americy's shore.
   Scrub the mud off the deadman's face** an' haul or ye'll
   be damned,
   For there blows some cold nor'westers on the Banks o'
   Newf'n'land.'

6. An' now we're off of the Hook, me boys, an' the land's all
   hid wid snow.
   Soon we'll see the pay-table, an' spend all nights below.
   Down to the docks they come in flocks, them pretty
   young gals do stand,
   Saying, 'It's snugger wid me than it is at sea, on the Banks
   of Newf'n'land!'

*Marry-bone: A suburb of Liverpool named Marybone
**Deadman's face: A hefty triangular plate with a hole in each corner.
Used for the purpose of mooring a ship between two anchors. The port

and starboard anchor chains were each made fast to the bottom holes, and the single chain leading in over the bow was attached to the top hole by way of a swivel to prevent the anchor chains twisting with the swing of each tide.

# The Bosun's Alphabet

1. A is for the Anchor that lies at our bow.
   B is for the Bowsprit an' the jibs all lie low.
   Oh! C is for the Capstan we all run around.
   D is for the Davits to low'r the boats down.
   *Sooo! Merrily, so merrily, so merrily sail we.*
   *There's no mortal on earth like a sailor at sea.*
   *Blow high or blow low! As the ship rolls along,*
   *Give a sailor his grog an' there's nothin' goes wrong!*

2. E is for the Earring when reefing we haul.
   F is for the Fo'c'sle where the bullies do brawl.
   Oh! G is for the Galley where the saltjunk smells strong.
   H is for the Halyards we hoist with a song.

3. I is for the Eyebolt – no good for the feet.
   J is for the Jibs, boys, stand by the lee sheet.
   Oh! K is for the Knightheads where the shantyman stands.
   L is for the Leeside hard found by new hands.

4. M is for the Maindeck – as white as new snow.
   N is for the Nigger gals in the land to which we go.
   Oh! O is for the Orlop, 'neath the 'tweendecks it lays.
   P is for the Peter flown on sailin' day.

5. Q is for the Quadrant – to the wheel it lies near.
   R is for the Rudder – it helps us to steer.
   Oh! S is for the Sheerpole over which we must climb.
   T is for the Topmen, 'way aloft everytime.

6. U is for Uniform – only worn aft.
   V is for the Vangs* running from the main gaff.
   Oh! W is for the Water – we're on pint and pound.
   X marks the Spot where Ol' Stormy wuz drown'd.

7. Y is for the Yard-arm – needs a good sailorman.
   Z is for Zoe – I'm her fancy-man.
   So this is the end of me bully ol' song.
   Heave away, buckos, oh, heave long an' strong!

*Vangs: Just as a boom is hauled from side to side by the sheets, so the gaff has ropes running either side from the peak so that this too can be trimmed to the wind like the boom.

# The Ebenezer

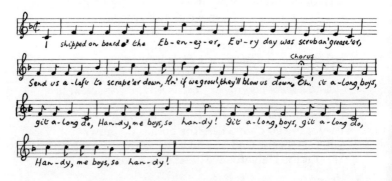

1. I shipped on board o' the Ebenezer.
   Every day 'twas scrub an' grease 'er,
   Send us aloft to scrape 'er down,
   An' if we growl, they'll blow us down.

*Oh! Git along, boys, git along do,*
*Handy, me boys, so handy!*
*Git along, boys, git along do,*
*Handy, me boys, so handy!*

2. The Ol' Man wuz a drunken geezer,
   Couldn't sail the Ebenezer;
   Learnt 'is trade on a Chinese junk,
   Spent most time, sir, in his bunk.

3. The chief mate's name wuz Dickie Green, sir,
   The dirtiest bugger ye've ever seen, sir;
   Walkin' his poop wid a bucko's roll,
   May the sharks 'ave 'is body, an' the Devil 'ave 'is soul.

4. A Boston buck wuz second greaser,
   He used to ship in lime juice ships, sir.
   The Limey packets got too hot,
   He jumped 'em, an' he cussed the lot.

5. The bosun came from Tennessee, sir,
   He always wore a Blackball cheeser*;
   He had a gal in every port,
   At least that's what 'is ol' wife thought.

6. The Ebenezer wuz so old, sir,
   She knew Columbus as a boy, sir;
   'Twas pump 'er bullies, night an' day,
   'To help 'er git to Liverpool Bay.

7. Wet hash it wuz our only grub, sir,
   For breakfast, dinner an' for supper;
   Our bread wuz as tough as any brass,
   An' the meat wuz as salt as Lot's wife's ass.

8. We sailed away before a breezer,
   Bound away for Vallaparaiser;
   Off the Horn she lost her sticks,
   The molly-hawks picked up the bits.

*Blackball Cheeser: A shiny peaked cap worn by mates serving on Blackball Line ships. A badge of authority identifying what was one of the more prestigious shipping companies.

# The Fire Ship

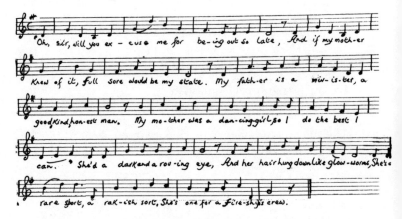

1. 'Oh sir, will you excuse me for being out so late,
   And if my mother knew of it, full sore would be my state.
   My father is a minister, a good, kind, honest man.
   My mother was a dancing-girl, so I do the best I can.'
       *She'd a dark and a roving eye.*
       *And her hair hung down like glow-worms.*
       *She's a rare sport, a rakish sort.*
       *She's one for a fireship's crew.*

2. I eyed the wench full warily, for talk like this I knew.
   She seemed a trifle o'er bold, she lied for all I knew.
   But still she wuz a comely wench – her lips a ruby red,
   Her bosom full, her hips were slim, she coyly hung her head.

3. And so I deemed her company for a sailor man like me.
   I goosed her, an' she goosed me back. Said she, 'Be kind to me!'
   I fondled her, I dandled her, I bounced her on my knee.
   She wept, she sighed and then she cried, 'Lud! Tell me, sir of your sea-ea-ea!'

# The Flying Cloud

1. My name is Edward Hollander, as you may understand.
   I was born in the city of Waterford in Erin's lovely land,
   When I was young and in me prime an' beauty on me shone,
   Me parents doted on me, 'cos I was their only son.

2. My father he rose up one morn an' wid him did I go.
   He bound me as a butcher boy to Kearney's of Wicklow.
   I wore the bloody apron there for three long years or more,
   Then I shipped aboard the Erin's Queen, the pride of ol' Tramore.

3. 'Twas when we reached Bermuda's Isle I met wid Cap'n Moore,
   The master o' the Flying Cloud, the pride of Baltimore;
   An' I undertook to sail wid him, on a slavin' voyage to go,
   To the burnin' shores o' Africy, where di sugar-cane do grow.

4. Oh, all went well until we came to Africy's sunny shore,
   Five hun'red o' them slaves, me boys, from their native land we bore.
   Oh, each man loaded down wid chains as we made 'em march below.
   Just eighteen inches space, me boy, oh, each man had to show.

5. The plague it came, an' fever too, an' took 'em off like
   flies.
   We had the niggers up on deck an' hove 'em in the tide.
   'Twas better for the rest o' them if they had died before.
   Than to drag the chain and feel the lash in Cuba for
   evermore.

6. An' now our money is all gone we must go to sea for
   more,
   So each man stayed an' listen'd to the words o' Cap'n
   Moore:
   'There's gold an' silver to be had, if with me you remain,
   Let's hoist the pirate flag aloft an' sweep the Spanish
   Main!'

7. We sank an' plundered many a ship down on the
   Spanish Main,
   Left many a wife an' orphan child in sorrow to remain.
   To them we gave no quarter but we gave them watery
   graves,
   For a sayin' of our Cap'n was that dead men tell no tales.

8. Pursued were we by many a ship, by frigates and liners
   too,
   Until a British man-o'-war, the Dungemore, hove in
   view.
   A shot then killed our Cap'n Moore an' twenty of our
   men,
   An' a bomb-shell set our ship on fire; we had to surrender
   then.

9. An' now to Newgate we must go, bound down wid iron
   chains,
   For the sinkin' an' the plunderin' of ships on the Spanish
   Main;
   The judge he found us guilty, an' we are condemned to
   die.
   Young man a warnin' by me take an' shun all piracy!

# The Gals Around Cape Horn

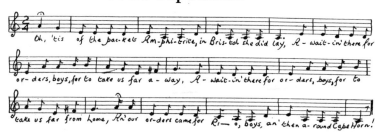

1. Oh, 'tis of the packet Amphitrite, in Bristol she did lay,
   Awaitin' there for orders, boys, for to take us far away,
   Awaitin' there for orders, boys, for to take us far from home,
   An' our orders came for Rio, boys, an' then around Cape Horn.

2. Oh, we beat our way across the Bay, with a fair wind to the Line,
   The royals all set and the stays all taut, the Trades they blew so fine;
   Our Johns they all were fighting fit, good seamen all were we,
   For to hand and reef and steer, me boys, we all worked bravely.

3. When we arrived in Rio, boys, we anchored there a while,
   We set up all our rigging, and we bent all our new sail;
   From ship to ship they cheered us, as we did pass along,
   And they wished us pleasant weather in a-roundin' o' the Horn.

4. When beatin' off Magellan Straits, the wind blew strong an' hard,
   While short'ning sail two gallant tars fell from the tops'l yard;
   By angry seas the lines we threw from their weak hands was torn,
   We had to leave 'em to the sharks that prowl around Cape Horn.

5. When we got round the Horn, me lads, fine nights and

pleasant days,
And the very next place we anchored in was Valparaiso
Bay,
Where all them pretty gals come down, I solemnly do
swear.
Oh, they're far above them Liverpool gals, with their
dark and wavy hair.

6. They like a jolly sailorman when he is on the spree,
They'll dance with you and drink with you and spend
yer money free,
And when yer money is all gone, they'll not on you
impose.
Oh, they're far above them Yankee gals who'll steal an'
pawn yer clothes.

7. Farewell to Valparaiso, boys, along the Chile main,
And likewise all them Spanish gals, they treated me just
fine;
An' if I live to get paid off, I'll sit and drink all morn,
A health to them dashing Spanish gals that live around
Cape Horn!

# Goodbye, Fare-Ye-Well

1. Oh, don't yez hear the Old Man say?
   *Goodbye, fare-ye-well! Goodbye, fare-ye-well!*
   Oh, don't yez hear the Old Man say?
   *Hoorah, me boys, we're homeward bound!*

2. We're homeward bound to Liverpool town,
   Where all them judies they will come down.

3. An' when we gits to the Wallasey Gates,
    Sally an' Polly for their flashmen do wait.

4. An' one to the other ye'll hear them say,
    'Here comes Johnny wid his fourteen months' pay.'

5. Them gals there on Lime Street we soon hope to meet.
    Soon we'll be a-rollin' both sides o' the street.

6. We'll meet these fly judies an' we'll ring the ol' bell,
    With them judies we'll meet there, we'll raise merry hell.

7. I'll tell me ol' mammy when I gits back home,
    The gals there on Lime Street won't leave me alone.

8. We're homeward bound to the gals of the town.
    Then heave away, bullies, we're all homeward bound.

9. We're a fine, flashy packet an' bound for to go,
    Wid them gals on the towrope she cannot say no.

10. We're homeward bound, we'll have yez to know,
    An' over the water to Liverpool must go.

# High Barbaree

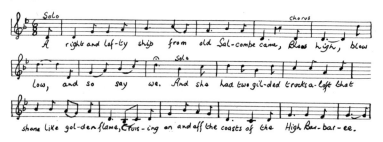

1. A right and lofty ship from old Salcombe came,
    *Blow high, blow low, and so say we.*
    And she had two gilded trucks aloft that shone like
    golden flame,
    *Cruising on and off the coasts of the High Barbaree.*

2. She was a gallant frigate-ship as ever sailed the sea,
   And her captain was a-searching for a pirate enemy.

3. Aloft there at the mastheads just haul all you can see,
   And keep look-out to windward and a look-out to your lee.

4. 'Mastheads aloft there,' was the capt'n's hail,
   'Look out around you. D'ye see a sail?'

5. I've been looking out to windward, but nothing can I see,
   But to leeward there's a lofty ship that's sailing fast and free.

6. She's a ship what looms like Beachy Head,
   Her banner aloft it blows out red.

7. The Capt'n hailed the stranger that was sailing on our lee,
   'Are you a foreign man-o'-war or a privateer?' said he.

8. 'I am neither one of two,' said she,
   'I'm a pirate ship a-looking for a fee.

9. 'I'm a roving pirate out for gold,
   I will rummage through your after hold.'

10. So we poured a broadside into her with the guns upon our lee,
    And we cut away his pirate masts and shot them in the sea.

11. The grumbling guns they flashed and roared,
    Till the pirate poop was overboard.

12. We fired shot till the pirate's deck,
    Was blood and spars and broken deck.

13. 'Give quarter,' cried the pirate chief, 'Give quarter unto me,'
    But no quarter did we give him, and we sank him in the sea.

14. He called for cans of wine and drank,

He sang his songs until she sank.

15. 'Oh, do not haul my red flag down,
    Oh, keep all fast until we drown.'

16. So let us brew good cans of flip,
    And drink a bowl to the Salcombe ship.

# Leave 'er, Johnny, Leave 'er

1. Oh, heave away, me bully boys.
   *Leave 'er, Johnny, leave 'er!*
   Oh, pump away an' make some noise.
   *Time for us ter leave 'er!*

2. Though times is hard, an' the wages low,
   There's a fathom o' water in the hold.

3. Oh, a dollar a day is a Jackshite's pay,
   To pump all night an' work all day.

4. The Ol' Man shouts, the pumps stand by.
   Oh, we can niver suck her dry.

5. Heave one more turn an' round she goes,
   Or each man jack will be kickin' up his toes.

6. 'It's pump or drown,' the Ol' Man said,
   'Or else damn soon ye'll all be dead.'

7. Heave around or we shall drown.
   Hey, don't yez feel her settlin' down?

8. Heave around them pump-bowls bright.
   There'll be no sleep for us this night.

9.  The rats have gone, an' we the crew,
    It's time, me boys, that we went too.

10. Leave 'er, Johnny, we can pump no more,
    It's time we wuz upon dry shore.

## Paddy West

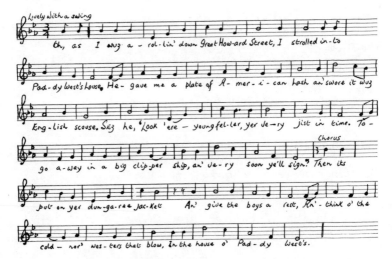

1.  Oh, as I wuz a-rollin' down Great Howard Street,
    I strolled into Paddy West's house.
    He gave me a plate of American hash
    An' swore it wuz English scouse.
    Sez he, 'Look 'ere, young feller, yer very jist in time
    To go away in a big clipper ship, an' very soon ye'll sign.'
        *Then it's put on yer dungaree jacket*
        *An' give the boys a rest,*
        *An' think o' the cold nor'westers that blow*
        *In the house o' Paddy West's!*

2.  Now he axed me if I had ever bin to sea.
    I told him not till that morn.
    'Well, be Jasus,' sez he, 'a sailor ye'll be,
    From the hour that yez wuz born;
    Just go into the parlour, walk round the ol' cow horn,

An' tell the mate that ye have bin, oh, three times round
the Horn!'

3. When I got into ol' Paddy West's house,
   The wind began to blow;
   He sent me up to the lumber-room,
   The fore-royal for to stow;
   When I climbed up to the attic, no fore-royal could I find,
   So I jumped upon the winder-sill and furled the winder-
   blind.

4. It's Paddy, me bhoy, he pipes all hands on deck,
   Their stations for to man.
   His wife, Sarry Ann, stood in the backyard,
   A bucket in her hand;
   His wife let go of the bucket, the water flew on its way;
   'Clew up yer fore-t'gallant, me sons, she's takin' in a stay!'

5. To every two men what graduates,
   I'll give wan outfit free.
   For two good men on watch at once
   Ye niver need to see.
   Oilskins, me bhoys, ye won't want, carpet slippers made
   o' felt,
   I will dish out to the pair o' ye, wid a ropeyarn for a belt.

# Ratcliffe Highway

1. As I wuz a-rollin' down the highway one morn,
   I spied a flash packet from ol' Wappin' tarn.
   As soon as I seed her, I slacked me mainbrace,

An' I hoisted me stuns'ls an' to her gave chase.
   *Oh, me riggin's slack,*
   *An' me rattlin's are frayed.*
   *I've rattled me riggin' down Ratcliffe Highway!*

2. Her flag wuz three colours, her masthead wuz low;
   She wuz round at the counter an' bluff at the bow;
   From larboard to starboard an' so rolled she;
   She wuz sailin' at large, she wuz running free.

3. I fired me bow-chaser, the signal she knew;
   She backed her main tops'l an' for me hove to;
   I lowered down me jollyboat an' rowed alongside,
   An' I found madam's gangway wuz open an' wide.

4. I hailed her in English; she answered me clear,
   'I'm from the Black Arrow bound to the Shakespeare';
   So I wore ship wid a what d'yer know,
   An' I passed her me hawser an' took her in tow.

5. I tipped her me flipper, me towrope an' all,
   She then let her hand on me reef-tackle fall;
   She then took me up to her lily-white room.
   An' in her main riggin' I fouled me jib boom.

6. I entered her little cubby hole, an' swore Damn yer eyes'.
   She wuz nothin' but a fireship rigged up in disguise.
   She had a foul bottom, from sternpost to fore,
   'Tween wind and water she ran me ashore.

7. She set fire to me riggin', as well as me hull,
   An' away to the lazareet I had to scull;
   Wid me helm hard-a-starboard as I rolled along,
   Me shipmates cried, 'Hey, Jack, yer mainyard is sprung!'

8. Now I'm safe in harbour, me moorings all fast,
   I lay here quite snug, boys, till all danger is past.
   With me mainyard all served, boys, an' parcelled an'
   tarred,
   Wasn't that a stiff breeze, boys, that sprung me
   mainyard?

9. Here's a health to the gal wid the black, curly locks;
   Here's a health to the gal who ran me on the rocks;

Here's a health to the quack, boys, who eased me from pain.
If I meet that flash packet I'll board her again.

# Rolling Home

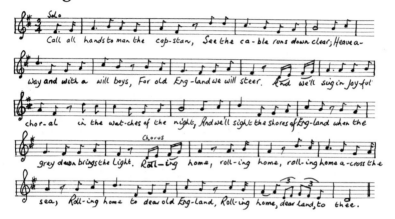

1. Call all hands to man the capstan,
   See the cable runs down clear;
   Heave away, and with a will, boys,
   For old England we will steer.
   And we'll sing in joyful choral in the watches of the night,
   And we'll sight the shores of England when the grey dawn brings the light.
   *Rolling home, rolling home, rolling home across the sea,*
   *Rolling home to dear old England,*
   *Rolling home, dear land, to thee.*

2. Up aloft, amid the rigging,
   Howls the wild, exultant gale;
   Like a bird's wide-outstretched pinions,
   Spreads on high each swelling sail,
   Seem to murmur as they flow,
   There are loving hearts that wait you
   In the land to which you go.

3. Many thousand miles behind us,
   Many thousand miles before;
   Mother ocean heaves to waft us

To a well-remembered shore;
Cheer up, lads, bright smiles await you,
From the fairest of the fair;
And sweet loving eyes will greet you,
With kind welcome everywhere.

## Rondo for Sledging

For we're shy, single, disengaged, free as the stars above.
Yes, we're shy, single, disengaged, looking for someone to
love.
There be rabbits in the mountains, shepherds in the hills,
But red-headed Kitty sets the pace that kills.
So we're shy, single, disengaged, looking for someone to
love.

## The Sailor's Way

1. We've courted gay Peruvian gals, French gals an'
   Chinee,
   Spanish gals an' Dutch gals too, an' dainty Japanee;
   To far Australia, Honolulu, where th' Hawaiian
   maidens play,
   Just a diff'rent gal in every port, *an' that's the sailor's way!*
     *Then it's goodbye, acushla, we're off to sea again.*
     *Sailor Jack always comes back to the gal he's left behind!*

2. In calm or storm, in rain or shine, the shellback doesn't
   mind,
   When on the ocean swell, he'll work like hell, for the gal
   he's left behind.
   He beats it north, he runs far south, he doesn't get
   much pay,
   He's always on a losin' game, *an' that's the sailor's way!*

3. Oh, shinin' is the North Star, as it hangs on our starb'd
   bow,
   We're homeward bound for Liverpool town, an' our
   hearts are in it now;
   We've crossed the Line an' the Gulf Stream, bin round
   by Table Bay,
   We've rounded Cape Horn, we're home again, *an' that's
   the sailor's way!*

4. We'll get paid off in Liverpool, an' blow our money free,
   We'll eat an' drink an' have our fun an' forget the
   god'am sea;
   Oh, Johnny'll go to his sweet Marie, an' Pat wid
   'is 'cushla play,
   But I'll get drunk, turn into me bunk, *an' THAT's the
   sailor's way!*

# Salt Beef

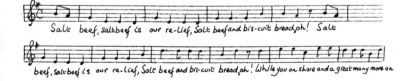

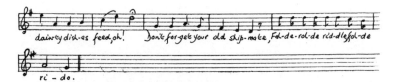

dainty dishes feed, oh! Don't forget your old ship-mate, Fol-de-rol-de-rid-dle fol-de

ri - do.

1. Salt beef, salt beef is our relief,
   Salt beef and biscuit bread, oh!
   Salt beef, salt beef is our relief,
   Salt beef and biscuit bread, oh!
   While you on shore and a great many more
   On dainty dishes feed, oh!
   Don't forget your old shipmate,
   Fol-de-rol-de-riddle, fol-de-ri-do!

2. Our hammocks they swing wet and cold,
   But in them we must lie, oh!
   Our hammocks they swing wet and cold,
   But in them we must lie, oh!
   While you on shore and a great many more,
   Are sleeping warm and dry, oh!
   Don't forget your old shipmate,
   Fol-de-rol-de-riddle, fol-de-ri-do!

# The Saucy Arabella

Oh! the Ar-a-bel-a set her main top-sail, The Ar-a-bel-a set her main

top-sail, The Ar-a-bel-a set her main top-sail, A-roll-ing

down the ri-ver. A-roll-ing down, a-roll-ing down, a-roll-ing

down the ri-ver, A-roll-ing down, a-roll-ing down, said the buck-o

mate to the greas-er's wife. Oh, a pump-kin pud-din an' a bul-gine pie, A

pump-kin pud-ding an' a bulg-ine pie, A pump-kin pud-ding an' a bul-gine pie, A-board the A-ra-bel-a!

1. Oh! the Arabella set her main topsail,
   The Arabella set her main topsail,
   The Arabella set her main topsail,
   A-rolling down the river.
   *A-rolling down, a-rolling down, a-rolling down the river,*
   *A-rolling down, a-rolling down, said the bucko mate to the greaser's wife.*

   *Oh, a pumpkin pudding an' a bulgine pie,*
   *A pumpkin pudding an' a bulgine pie,*
   *A pumpkin pudding an' a bulgine pie,*
   *A-board the Arabella!*

2. So the Arabella set her main staysail,
   The Arabella set her main staysail,
   The Arabella set her main staysail,
   A-rolling down the river.

3. Oh, the Arabella set her …

   The shantyman would include every sail in the ship's
   wardrobe and a few more besides until the sail change
   had been completed.

# Spanish Ladies

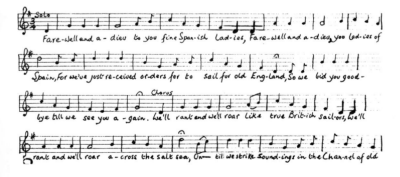

Fare-well and a-dieu to you fine Span-ish Lad-ies, Fare-well and a-dieu yoo lad-ies of Spain, for we've just re-ceived or-ders for to sail for old Eng-land, So we bid you good-bye till we see you a-gain. We'll rant and we'll roar like true Brit-ish sail-ors, we'll rant and we'll roar a-cross the salt sea, Un— til we strike Sound-ings in the Chan-nel of old

1. Farewell and adieu to you fine Spanish ladies,
   Farewell and adieu, you ladies of Spain,
   For we've just received orders for to sail for old England,
   So we bid you goodbye till we see you again.
       *We'll rant and we'll roar like true British sailors,*
       *We'll rant and we'll roar across the salt sea,*
       *Until we strike soundings in the Channel of old England.*
       *From Ushant to Scilly 'tis thirty-five leagues.*

2. We hove our ship to, with the wind to the sou'west,
   We hove our ship to, for to strike soundings clear,
   And we found forty fathoms, on a fine sandy bottom,
   So we filled our main-tops'l up Channel to steer.

3. And the first land we sighted, it is called the Deadman,
   Next Ram Head, off Plymouth, Start, Portland and Wight,
   Then we squared away up-Channel by Fairlee and Dungeness,
   And then bore away for the South Foreland's Light.

4. Then the signal was made for the whole fleet to anchor,
   All in the Downs that night for to meet.
   Then stand-by yer ring-stoppers an' let go yer shank painters!
   Haul up yer clew-garnets! Let go tacks and sheets!

5. Now let every man take up his full bumper,
   Let every take up his full bowl,
   For we will be jolly an' drown melancholy
   With a health to each jovial an' true-hearted soul.
       *An' we'll rant and we'll roar like true British sailors,*
       *We'll rant and we'll roar across the salt seas,*
       *Until we strike soundings in the Channel of old England.*
       *From Ushant to Scilly 'tis thirty-five leagues.*

After the last line, shout: *'Heave – An' – Bust 'Er!'*

# The Stately Southerner

1. Oh, it was a stately Southerner, as flew the stars and
   bars,
   An' the whistlin' wind from the west-nor'-west rang
   thro' her pitch-pine spars,
   And with her tacks about, me boys, she hung upon the
   gale.
   'Twas an autumn night when she made the light of the
   ol' Head o' Kinsale.

2. It was a fine an' cloudless night, the wind blew fresh an'
   strong,
   As gaily 'cross the Channel wave our good ship bowl'd
   along;
   An' the foam beneath her tramplin' bows the rollin'
   waves did spread,
   An' as she stooped low, with her breast o' snow, she
   buried her lee cathead.

3. There was no talk of short'ning sail by him who trod the
   poop,
   And under the weight of the ponderous jib her boom
   bent like a hoop;
   An' the groaning chesstrees* told the strain held down
   by the stout main tack,
   But he only laughed as he gazed abaft at her bright an'
   glitterin' track.

4. The mid-tide met in Channel waves that flow from
   shore to shore,

The mist lay thick along the land from Featherstone to Dunmore;
Yet gleamed the light on Tuskar Rock where the bell still tolled the hour,
But the beacon light that shone so bright was quenched on Waterford Tower.

5. The canvas that our good ship bore was tops'ls fore an' aft,
   Her spanker** too and standing jib, for she was a stiffish craft;
   'All hands aloft!' our Old Man cried. 'Loose out yer light sail fast!'
   And t'gans'ls all an' royals small soon swelled upon each mast.

6. What looms upon our starboard bow, what hands upon the breeze?
   'Tis time the packet hauled her wind abreast the old Saltees;
   For by the mighty press of sail that clothed each lofty spar,
   That ship we spied on the misty tide was a British man-o'-war.

7. 'Out booms, out booms!' our skipper cried. 'Out booms an' give her sheet!'
   And the swiftest keel that ever was launched shot ahead of the British fleet;
   And amidst a thundering shower o' shot, with stuns'ls hoistin' away,
   Down Channel clear, Paul Jones did steer, just at the break o' day.

*Chesstrees: A wooden block with several sheaves, fitted to the bulwarks or to the forecastle head, through which the tack of the mainsail or foresail was rove for heaving down the weather clew. Not in existence in the later sailing ships but mentioned in ships of the eighteenth and early nineteenth centuries.
**Spanker: The lower fore and aft sail on the after mast of a barque or ship. Sometimes referred to as a driver.

# The Whale

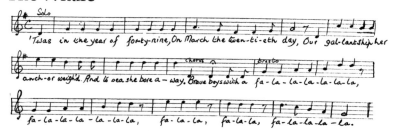

1. 'Twas in the year of forty-nine,
   On March the twentieth day,
   Our gallant ship her anchor weigh'd
   And to sea she bore away.
   *Brave boys with a fa-la-la-la-la-la-la,*
   *Fa-la-la-la-la-la-la, fa-la-la, fa-la-la,*
   *Fa-la-la-la-la.*

2. 'Old Blowhard' was our Cap'n's name,
   Our ship the Teaser bold,
   And we were bound to the North Country,
   To face the frost and the cold.

3. And then we came to that cold country,
   Where the ice and the snow do lie,
   Where there's ice and snow, and the great whales blow,
   And the daylight does not die.

4. Our mate went up to the topmast cap
   With a spy-glass in his hand.
   'A whale, a whale, a whale,' he cries,
   'And she spouts at every span.'

5. Up jumped old Blowhard from the deck,
   And a clear little man was he:
   'Overhaul, overhaul, let your maintackle fall,
   And launch your boat to sea.'

6. We struck that fish and away she flew,
   With a flourish of her tail,
   But oh! and alas! we lost a man,
   And we did not catch that whale.

7. Now when the news to our Cap'n came,

He called up all his crew,
And, for the losing of that man,
He down our colours drew.

8. Says he, 'My man, be not dismayed
   At the losing of one man,
   For Providence will have his will,
   Let man do what he can.'

9. Now the losing of that 'prentice hand,
   It grieved our skipper sore,
   But the losing of that great big whale
   Grieved him a damned sight more.

# 7   Broadside Ballads

Arethusa, The
Golden Vanity, The
Heart of Oak
Mermaid, The
Portsmouth
Rude Boreas
Rule Britannia
Tom Bowling

In past centuries, in the principal cities, up-to-date news of current events was conveyed to the public at large by street vendors distributing news items written on sheets of flimsy paper called broadsheets.

It is not surprising that maritime matters, battles and victories were a constant feature of the broadsheets in the eighteenth century, since Britain was engaged in wars with the Dutch, French and Spanish, and later with the American colonists, and waging an interminable campaign against privateers and pirates, establishing new colonies and developing and extending trade routes.

The broadsheets owed much of their popularity to national patriotism and to a thirst for reading of contemptuous deeds of daring and bravery in the face of overwhelming odds – a trait endemic in a nation newly acquiring a reputation as the world's foremost sea power. This arrogant national fervour was eagerly encouraged by street ballad-makers and art-song writers, who produced their own broadsheets of patriotic ballads extolling the heroes of the broadsheet news items. These ballads were often no more than a simple adaptation lifted from a prose broadsheet and soon became known as broadside ballads.

These glowing reports, often more enthusiastically than accurately compiled, and the stirring ballads which emerged to be sung in the public houses and music halls of the period, excited and inspired the whole nation and encouraged a spirit of adventure and selfless courage, so that future generations of Englishmen followed the example of their predecessors whose superstar qualities had been recorded by broadsheet and ballad.

It must be admitted that the majority of the broadside ballads, although certainly *inspired* by the sea and by the exploits of English seamen, did not originate on board ship and definitely not from the sailors themselves. Many of the ballads abused and derided the sailors of other nations – something the English sailor would never do, for sailors of all nations sharing the common dangers of the sea held a mutual respect for each other. The ballads were not suitable as shanties and certainly did not express the true sentiments of the seamen and therefore would not be sung as forebitters.

The following ballads are included to illustrate the sentiments expressed in the broadsheet-inspired sea-songs, and it will be readily appreciated that considerable creative licence was used and produced utterly misleading ideas of the conditions under which the sailors of the day lived and fought. However, as inspiring and recruiting media they were certainly effective.

## The Arethusa

Come all ye jol-ly Sail-ors bold, Whose hearts are cast in hon-our's mould, While Eng-lish glo-ry I un-fold, Hur-ra for the A-re-thu-sa! She is a fri-gate tight and brave, As ev-er stemm'd the dash-ing wave, Her men are staunch to their fa-v'rite launch, And when the foe shall

1. Come all ye jolly sailors bold,
   Whose hearts are cast in honour's mould,
   While English glory I unfold,
   Hurra for the Arethusa!
   She is a frigate tight and brave,
   As ever stemm'd the dashing wave;
   Her men are staunch to their fav'rite launch,
   And when the foe shall meet our fire,
   Sooner than strike we'll all expire,
   On board of the Arethusa.

2. 'Twas with the spring fleet she went out,
   The English Channel to cruise about,
   When four French sail, in show so stout,
   Bore down on the Arethusa.
   The famed Belle Poule straight ahead did lie,
   The Arethusa seem'd to fly,
   Not a sheet, or a tack,
   Or brace did she slack,
   Tho' the Frenchmen laugh'd and thought it stuff,
   But they knew not the handful of men, so tough,
   On board of the Arethusa.

3. On deck five hundred men did dance,
   The stoutest they could find in France;
   We with two hundred did advance,
   On board the Arethusa.
   Our Capt'n hailed the Frenchman, 'Ho!'
   The Frenchman then cried out, 'Hallo!'
   'Bear down, d'ye see,
   To our Admiral's lee!'
   'No, no!' says the Frenchman, 'That can't be!'

'Then I must lug you along with me,'
Says the saucy Arethusa.

4.  The fight was off the Frenchman's land,
    We drove them back upon their strand,
    For we fought till not a stick could stand
    Of the gallant Arethusa.
    And we've driv'n the foe ashore,
    Never to fight with Britons more.
    Let each fill a glass
    To his fav'rite lass:
    A health to the Capt'n and officers true,
    And all that belong to the jovial crew
    On board of the Arethusa.

# The Golden Vanity

1.  O, I have a ship in the North countree,
    And she goes by the name of the Golden Vanity;

I'm afraid she will be taken by some Turkish gallilee
As she sails along the Lowlands low,
   *Lowlands, Lowlands,*
   *As she sails along the Lowlands low.*

2. And then up started our little cabin boy,
   Saying, 'What will you give me if the galley I destroy?
   Will you give me of your treasure, if I sink the gallilee,
   If I sink her in the Lowlands low?'

3. 'I will give you gold, I will give you of my store,
   And my daughter you shall marry when we return to
   shore,
   If you sink the Turkish ship to the bottom of the sea,
   If you sink her in the Lowlands low.'

4. The boy bent his breast and he jumped into the sea,
   Taking with him an auger from the Golden Vanity,
   And he swam until he came to the Turkish gallilee,
   As she lay in the Lowlands low.

5. He bored with his auger two holes in a trice,
   While some were playing cards, and some were playing
   dice,
   And he let the water in, and it dazzled in their eyes,
   And he sank them in the Lowlands low.

6. He swam back again to the Golden Vanity,
   Saying, 'Master, take me up. I am drowning in the sea.
   For the Turkish ship is sunk, from all peril we are free,
   I have sunk her in the Lowlands low.'

7. 'I'll not take thee up, nor give you of my store,
   My daughter you shall not marry, when I come to shore,
   I will kill you, I will shoot you, I will send you with the
   tide,
   I will drown you in the Lowlands low.'

8. The boy swam around to the starboard side,
   Saying, 'Shipmates, pick me up, I am drowning with the
   tide.'
   And they laid him on the deck, and then, alas! he died,
   And they sank him in the Lowlands low.

# Heart of Oak

1. Come, cheer up, my lads, 'tis to glory we steer,
   To add something more to this wonderful year*;
   To honour we call you, not press you like slaves,
   For who are so free as the sons of the waves?
   *Heart of oak are our ships, heart of oak are our men.*
   *We always are ready. Steady, boys, steady!*
   *We'll fight – and we'll conquer again and again.*

2. We ne'er see our foes but we wish them to stay,
   They never see us but they wish us away;
   If they run, why we follow and run them ashore,
   And if they won't fight us, we cannot do more.

3. Still Britain shall triumph, her ships plough the sea,
   Her standard be justice, her watchword 'Be free.'
   Then cheer up, my lads, with one heart let us sing,
   Our soldiers, our sailors, our statesmen and King.

*Verses written by David Garrick in 1759 to celebrate Hawke's victory of Quiberon Bay. Set to music by William Boyce. The rhythm was beaten by boy drummers to summon hands to quarters (battle stations) when the ship was preparing for action.

# The Mermaid

1. One Friday morn, when we set sail,
   And our ship not far from land,
   We there did espy a fair pretty maid,
   With a comb and a glass in her hand, her hand, her hand,
   With a comb and a glass in her hand.
   *While the raging seas did roar,*
   *And the stormy winds did blow,*
   *And we jolly sailor boys were up, up aloft,*
   *And the land-lubbers lying down below, below, below.*
   *And the land-lubbers lying down below.*

2. Then up spoke the captain of our gallant ship,
   Who at once our peril did see,
   'I have married a wife in fair London town,
   And this night she a widow will be.'

3. And then up spoke the little cabin boy,
   And a fair hair'd boy was he,
   'I've a father and mother in fair Portsmouth town,
   And this night they will weep for me.'

4. Then three times round went our gallant ship,
   And three times round went she;
   For the want of a lifeboat they all went down,
   As she sank to the bottom of the sea.

## Portsmouth

A lively tune without lyrics. Ideal for sailors gathered around the forebitts where they could exercise by dancing in the mistaken belief that vigorous exercise was a good antiscorbutic by encouraging the red blood cells to chase away the white cells.

## Rude Boreas

1. Come, rude Boreas, blust'ring railer, list ye landsmen all to me.
   Shipmates, hear a brother sailor sing of the dangers of the sea.
   From bounding billows, first in motion, when the distant whirlwinds rise,
   To the tempest-troubled ocean, when the skies contend with skies.

2. Hark the bosun's hoarsely bawlin', 'By tops'l sheets an' halyards stand.
   Down t'gans'ls, quick, be haulin', down yer stays'ls, hard, boys, hard!

See it freshens, set taut the braces, tops'l sheets now let go,
Luff, boys, luff, don't make wry faces, up yer tops'ls nimbly clew.'

3. Now all ye on downbeds a-sportin', fondly locked in Beauty's arms,
Fresh enjoyments, wanton courtin', safe from all but love alarm;
Round us roars the angry tempest, see what fears our minds enthrall,
Harder yet, it blows still harder, hark again the bosun's call:

4. 'The tops'l yard points to the wind blows, see all clear to reef each course,
Let the foresheet go, don't mind boys, tho' the weather should be worse;
Fore 'n' aft the sprits'l yard get, reef the mizzen, see all clear,
Hands up each preventer-brace get, man the fore-yard, cheer, boys, cheer!'

5. All the while fierce thunder's roarin', peel on peel contendin' flash,
On our heads fierce rain falls pourin', in our eyes blue lightnings flash,
All around us one wide water, all above us one black sky,
Different deaths at once surround us. Hark! What means that dreadful cry?

6. 'The foremast's gone!' cries every tongue out, o'er the lee twelve foot above deck,
A leak there is beneath the chesstrees sprung, pipe all hands to clear the wreck;
Come, cut the lanyards all to pieces, come, me hearts, be stout an' bold,
Plumb the well, the leak increases, four foot o' water in the hold.

7. O'er the ship wild waves are beatin', we for wives and children moan,
Alas from here there's no retreatin', alas to them there's no return;

Still the leak is gainin' on us, both chain-pumps are fouled below,
Heaven have mercy here upon us, for only that can save us now.

8. On the lee beam there is land, boys, let the guns overboard be thrown,
To the pump come every hand, boys, see our mizzen mast is gone;
The leak we've found it can't pour faster, we've lightened her a foot or, more,
Up an' rig a jury foremast, she's right, she's right, boys, we're off shore.

9. Now once more on shore we're thinkin', since kind Heaven has saved our lives,
Come the cup now let's be drinkin' to our sweethearts an' our wives;
Fill it up, about ship wheel it, close to our lips a-brimmin' fine,
Where's the tempest now? Who feels it? None! the danger's drowned in wine!

# Rule Britannia

1. When Britain first at Heav'n's command,
   Arose from out the azure main,
   Arose, arose, arose from out the azure main,
   This was the charter, the charter of the land,
   And guardian angels sang the strain,
       *Rule Britannia! Britannia, rule the waves!*
       *Britons never, never, never shall be slaves.*

2. The nations not so blest as thee,
   Must in their turn to tyrants fall,
   While thou shalt flourish great and free,
   The dread and envy of them all.

3. Still more majestic shalt thou rise,
   More dreadful from each foreign stroke,
   As the loud blast that rends the skies,
   Serves but to root thy native oak.

4. The Muses still with freedom found,
   Shall to thy happy coast repair,
   Blest Isle with matchless beauty crown'd,
   And manly hearts to guard the fair.

# Tom Bowling

1. Here, a sheer hulk, lies poor Tom Bowling,
   The darling of our crew;
   No more he'll hear the tempest howling,
   For death has broached him to.
   His form was of the manliest beauty,
   His heart was kind and soft;
   Faithful below he did his duty,
   But now he's gone aloft, but now he's gone aloft.

2. Tom never from his word departed,
   His virtues were so rare;
   His friends were many and true-hearted,
   His Poll was kind and fair.
   And then he'd sing so blithe and jolly,
   Ah! many's the time and oft;
   But mirth is turned to melancholy,
   For Tom is gone aloft, for Tom is gone aloft.

3. Yet shall poor Tom find pleasant weather,
   When He, Who all commands,
   Shall give, to call life's crew together,
   The word to pipe all hands.
   Thus Death, who kings and tars despatches,
   In vain Tom's life has doff'd;
   For though his body's under hatches,
   His soul is gone aloft, his soul is gone aloft.

# 8   Fishermen's Ballads

Not all seamen were Sailor Johns or Jolly Jacks: the late seventeenth century, the eighteenth and nineteenth centuries and the early twentieth century saw vast fishing fleets at work around the coasts of the British Isles. Working ships, whether coastal brig, China clipper or fishing smack, had many similarities, and as the fishermen worked at the windlass and hauled and pumped they sang in the same circumstances as their messmates in other vessels. When fishing was bad, the fishermen would work in the coastal trade, and during the frequent wars which bedevilled the period they served in the King's ships, so shanty-singing was a familiar accompaniment to their work and when resting in the forecastle. Unashamedly they stole a number of rousing tunes and turned them into their own by adding their own verses and terminology which described the particular difficulties they experienced on the fishing grounds and on the specialized pieces of equipment with which they worked.

The following breezy fishermen's ballad lends itself to the music of the forebitter 'According to the Act', but it was sung with gusto to local interpretations of a number of other tunes as well.

1. Oh, once I wuz a schoolboy an' lived at home at ease,
   But now I am a fisherlad who ploughs the ragin' seas.
   I thought I'd like seafaring life, but very soon I found
   It wuz not all plain sailin' when we reach'd the fishin' ground.

*Heave away the trawl warp, boys, an' let's heave up our trawl,*
*For when we gets our fish on deck, we'll have another haul.*
*So heave away on the trawl warp, boys, and merrily heave*
*away.*
*For it's just as bright when the moon shines bright as 'tis at the*
*break o' day.*

2. Oh, every night in winter, as reg'lar as the clock,
   On gooze sou'wester, deep sea-boots and oilskin
   smock,
   Then straight away to the capstan, boys, and merrily
   heave away,
   For it's just as light in the middle of the night as 'tis at
   the break o' day.

3. Oh, when the eight weeks are over, hard up the tiller
   gooz,
   Sou'west by west for Yarmouth Roads with the big jib
   on the nose,
   An' when we reach the pierhead, all the gals they will
   say,
   'Here come our jolly fishin' lads that's been so long
   away.'

Another piece of fisherman's adaptation was sung to the
tune of 'A-Roving':

1. In Lowestoft a boat was laid,
   Mark well what I do say!
   An' she wuz built for the 'errin' trade,
   But she has gone a-rovin', and a-rovin',
   Round the North Sea rovin',
   The Lord knows where.

2. Her cook wuz chef in the lost dogs' home,
   Mark well what I do say!
   And I'm sorry for our hungry crew,
   They'd rather go a-rovin', a-rovin',
   Around the North Sea rovin',
   Than eat his lousy stew.

# 9 Bawdy Songs and Bilge-Water Ballads

A Clean Song
Backsides Rule the Navy
Bell-Bottom Trousers
Blow the Man Down
Christopher Columbus
Jenny Wren Bride
Lulu
There's Nothing Else To Do
Turalai
We Set Sail
Winnipeg Whore
You're a Liar

Vital people have experiences which generally inspire some kind of creative activity or expression, and Sailor John and Jolly Jack certainly fit into that category.

As we have already seen, the unremitting hardships and constant danger of shipboard life are well documented in the words and sentiments of the sailors' shanties. While the music lacked quality, being limited by the range of the crude instruments, and while the lyrics were coarse, reflecting the universal lack of education of the labouring classes during that period, nevertheless the ballads represented a very real expression of sailors' experiences.

The sailors were not wholly saints nor totally sinners. The awful might of nature's forces was beyond their simple understanding but they believed that God was a power who could control even greater forces than nature, and this gave them something to believe in and take comfort from. They were then for the most part 'God-fearing' – 'God respecting' would be a more appropriate term – but in no sense were they fervently religious. Although the very name 'sailor' was universally accepted as being synonymous when ashore with drunkenness, debauchery, whoring, lust and rapacity, the nature of their calling held them to a strict code which they were proud to uphold. They were certainly hard-working, courageous, loyal to their ship – intensely so to their shipmates, whom they regarded as fellow-sufferers.

The sailor was what he was through the conditioning of his calling and by his lowly station in the rigidly strata-ed class system of the period. He shared all the hardships of the oppressed labouring-class but with an additional burden: emotional expression, a vital part of life, was denied him for long periods. Whereas others could enjoy family life and emotional relationships, the sailor could indulge in them only for brief and infrequent periods – and in these, not unnaturally, being physical in his calling, he did to excess.

Shipboard life, monastic in its deprivations, certainly frustrated the sailors' natural feelings. With long voyages made even longer by prolonged calms in the Horse Latitudes, weather-bound in some hostile, fever-ridden bay, beating against perverse headwinds in unweatherly ships for weeks on end and with no shore leave at the end of it if you were a Jolly Jack (for fear of desertion), one's deprivations took on a desperate importance. So it was not surprising that ashore they loved and drank to excess, for the present was all too short and their next spell of liberty might never come.

When natural outlets were denied for long periods, unnatural outlets developed. The last port's amorous associations took on a disproportionate importance as memories were cherished with nostalgic and often magnified fervour. In some cases sexual perversion was the solution, but generally the men would talk, exaggerate and even lie to one another about their latest amorous adventures with women in order to rid themselves of their consuming frustrations.

From talking to writing and singing ballads immortalizing their amorous affairs was but a small step, and the following are a small collection of some of the bawdy songs that occupied many an uneasy dog-watch or an hour sheltering below decks soaked and freezing in a North Atlantic gale or enduring 'prickly heat' in the equatorial latitudes. Surprisingly, the songs were not always sung with tenderness and feeling but often yelled in defiance or seething frustration into the teeth of a storm or when pinned to a flat sea becalmed under a remorselessly burning sun a thousand miles from land.

The following then are a collection of 'ballads of frustration' which were sung, or yelled, by sailors all across the oceans. Their assonances and dissonances, their vulgarity and depravity, their rollicking humour and wry wit have been set down intact – and for that I offer no apology.

# A Clean Song

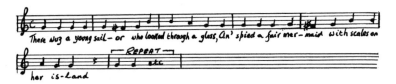

There wuz a young sailor who looked through a glass
  An' spied a fair mermaid with scales on her ISLAND
Where seagulls fly over their nests.
  She combed her long hair, which hung over her
SHOULDERS
An' caused her to tickle and itch.
  The sailor cried out, 'There's a beautiful MERMAID
A sitting out there on the rocks.'
  The crew came a-runnin', a-grabbing their GLASSES
An' crowded four-deep at the rail,
  All eager to share in this fine piece of NEWS
Which the Captain soon heard from the watch.
  He tied down the wheel and he reached for his
CRACKERS AND CHEESE
Which he kept near the door
  In case he might some day encounter a MERMAID.
He knew he must use all of his wits,
  Crying, 'Throw out a line! We'll lasso her FLIPPERS
And then we will certainly find
  If mermaids are better before or BE BRAVE:
'My good fellows,' the Captain then said.
  Good fortune will break through her Mermaiden
HEADING.
To starboard they tacked with despatch
  An' caught that fair mermaid just under the ELBOWS,
Then hustled her down between decks.
  Each took a turn at her feminine SETTING
Her free at the end of the farce.
  She splashed in the waves landing right on her AFTER
A while one man noticed some scabs.
  Soon they broke out with the pox and the
SCRATCHING
With fury, cursing with spleen.
  The song may be dull but it's certainly clean.

# Backsides Rule the Navy

*Backsides rule the Navy.*
*Backsides rules the sea.*
*If you want a bit of bum,*
*Better get it from me, chum.*
*Ye'll get no bum from me!*

1.  Let us sing a bit of good old Capt'n Kitt,
    Who sat one mornin' early in the Heads.
    A bee came flying past, stung him on the arse,
    An' this is what the gallant Cap'n said:

2.  Next we'll sing some rhymes of Yeoman Sydney
    Grimes,
    Who ran the hook that hoisted up the mail.
    One night as he stood watch, it caught him in the
    crotch,
    An' he cried as he went flying cross the rail.

3.  Now let us end our song with a look at AB Long,
    Whose member wasn't like his name at all.
    When asked if he would tell how he got on so well,
    His explanation wuz as I recall:

# Bell-Bottom Trousers

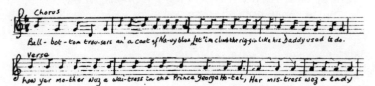

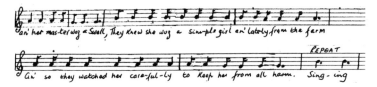

*Singing, a-bell-bottom trousers an' a coat of navy blue*
*Let him climb the rigging like his Daddy used to do.*

1. Now yer mother wuz a waitress in the Prince George Hotel.
   Her mistress wuz a lady, an' her master wuz a swell.
   They knew she wuz a simple girl an' lately from the farm,
   And so they watched her carefully to keep her from all harm.

2. The 47th Fusileers came marching into town,
   An' with them came a complement of rapists of renown.
   They busted every maidenhead that came within their spell,
   But they never made the waitress at the Prince George Hotel.

3. Next came a company of the Prince of Wales Hussars.
   They piled into the whorehouse and packed along the bars.
   Many a maiden, mistress and wife before them fell,
   But they never made the waitress at the Prince George Hotel.

4. One day there came a sailor, an ordinary bloke,
   Bulging out his trousers with a heart of solid oak.
   At sea without a woman for seven years or more,
   There was no need to ask what he was looking for.

5. He asked for a candlestick to light his way to bed,
   He asked for a pillow to rest his weary head,
   An' speaking very gently, just as if he meant no harm,
   He asked her if she'd come to bed just so's to keep him warm.

6. She lifted up the blankets and a moment there did lie.

He was on her, he was in her in the twinkling of an eye.
He was out again and in again and ploughing up a storm,
But the only words she said to him, 'I hope you're
keeping warm.'

7. Then early in the morning the sailor he arose,
   Saying here's a £2 note, my dear, for the damage I have
   caused.
   If you have a daughter, bounce her on yer knee.
   If you have a son, send the bastard off to sea.

8. And now she sits beside the dock, a baby on her knee,
   Waitin' for the sailing-ships a-comin' home from sea,
   Waitin' for the jolly tars in Navy uniforms,
   An' all she wants to do, my boys, is keep the Navy warm.

# Blow the Man Down

1. Oh, as I wuz a-rollin' down Paradise Street,
   *To me way, hay, blow the man down!*
   A handsome young damsel I chanc' fer to meet.
   *Oh! Gimme some time to blow the man down!*

2. She wuz round in the counter an' bluff in the bow,
   So I put on all steam, called 'Way hold-up now.'

3. I held out my flipper an' took her in tow
   An' yard-arm to yard-arm away we did go.

4. Said she to me, 'Sailor, will you stand treat?'
   'Delighted,' sez I, 'for a charmer so sweet.'

5. She drank down a pint, I swilled a quart.

She listed to starboard, I listed to port.

6. Well up in her quarters she piped me aboard,
   An' there on the bed I cut loose with me sword.

7. I ruffled her scuppers, I battered her stern,
   An' down in her galley I wuz done to a turn.

8. But just as me cutter was a-forging ahead
   She hollered, 'My husband!' and jumped out of bed.

9. He wuz seven feet tall with a chest like a horse,
   An' straight fer me jawbone he plotted a course.

10. He battered me rudder and loosened me stays,
    An' I flew down them stairs like a ship on the ways.

11. Well, I hopped on a packet that happened along,
    An' when I woke up I wuz bound fer Hong Kong.

12. So, young man, take warning afore you delay,
    Don't never pay heed to what pretty girls say.

# Christopher Columbus

*He knew the world was round-o,*
*His beard hung to the ground-o,*

*That navigatin', calculatin'*
*Son-of-a-gun Columbo.*

1. In fourteen hundred, ninety-two,
   A guy from old I-ta-lee
   Was walkin' thro' the streets of Spain,
   A-peddlin' hot Tomali.

2. He met the Queen of Spain and said,
   'Just give me ships and cargo,
   And hang me up until I'm dead
   If I don't bring back Chicago.'

3. 'Hey, take your time,' sez Isabel,
   'And don't forget essentials.
   Come with me to my bedroom, boy.
   I will check on your credentials.'

4. She gave her guest no time for rest,
   The pace was something wicked.
   Why every hour on the clock
   She punched Columbo's ticket.

5. For forty nights and forty days,
   They sailed the broad Atlantic.
   Columbo and his lousy crew
   For want of a tail were frantic.

6. Now Columbo had a one-eyed mate,
   He loved him like a brother,
   So every night at half-past-eight
   They buggered one another.

7. They spied a whore upon the dock,
   And on went coats and collars.
   In twenty minutes by the clock,
   She'd made ten thousand dollars.

8. Then with happy shout they ran about
   And practised fornication,
   And when they sailed, they left behind
   Ten times the population.

# Jenny Wren Bride

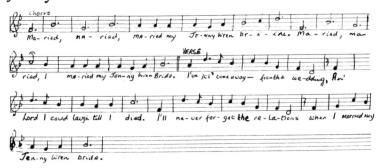

*Married, married, married my Jenny Wren bride.*
*Married, married, I married my Jenny Wren bride.*

1. I've jus' come away from the wedding,
   An' Lord I could laugh till I died.
   I'll never forget the relations
   When I married my Jenny Wren bride.

2. Her brother he works in the dockyards,
   Her Pa owns a mariner's store,
   An' out of their habits, they breed jus' like rabbits,
   An' own half the cradles on shore.

3. I asked her old man fer a dowry.
   He gave me a can of soft soap,
   A bundle of waste, an' some polishing paste
   An' fifty-four fathoms of rope.

4. Now the present I got from her sister
   Wuz some postal cards labelled 'obscene'.
   Her brother's a raper, he gives me some paper,
   Six packs of 'Service latrine'.

5. Her panties were made of pink coral,
   Her bra wuz two clams held wiv clips,
   While her suspenders were motorboat fenders,
   Hung from her navel in strips.

6. Now most of this strange congregation
   Wuz made up of Wrens lined in fours,

While in the back pew wuz a generous crew,
Of Portsmouth's favourite whores.

7.  So now we're off on the honeymoon.
I don't know what happens tonight,
But I have talked to a few who declare that they do,
An' they swear she's a bit of all right!

## Lulu

Bang away, Lulu,
*Bang her good an' strong.*
*What in the hell will the Navy do*
*When Lulu's dead and gone?*

1.  Now some girls work in factories,
Some girls work in stores,
But Lulu works in a dockside house
With forty other whores.

2.  Lulu had a baby,
It was her pride and joy,
Would have named it Lulu
But the bastard was a boy.

3. She took me to the picture show,
   We sat down in the stalls,
   An' every time the lights went out,
   She grabbed me by the nose.

4. She took me to the mountain top
   And laid me on the hill,
   Cos every time I said, 'I won't,'
   The echo said, 'I will'!

5. I wish I was a diamond ring
   On my little Lulu's hand,
   An' every time she scratched her ...
   I would see the promised land.

6. Well, I asked her for to marry me,
   She said, 'That's very nice,
   But I'll give you a better deal:
   I'll let you ride half price!'

# There's Nothing Else To Do

*Friggin' in the riggin', friggin' in the riggin',*
*Friggin' in the riggin', there's nothin' else to do!*

1. 'Twas back in 'sixty-nine,
   We left the Blackball Line.
   The crew did cry as we went by,
   An' we left our mates behind.

2. 'Twas back in '63,
   When the captain went to sea,
   Born from a whore, he wuz cast ashore,
   A son of a bitch wuz he.

3. A cook whose name wuz Davy,
   Wuz cashiered from the Navy.
   He dipped the bread inside the head
   An' served it up for gravy.

4. The bosun's mate was Andy,
   A Portsmouth man and randy.
   He used to dip his favourite tool
   In a glass of the skipper's brandy.

5. The captain's wife was Mable.
   As oft as she wuz able,
   Would give the crew a weekly screw
   Across the chart-room table.

6. The captain of our lugger,
   He wuz a dirty bugger.
   He wasn't fit to shovel grit
   From one ship to another.

7. The cabin-boy's name wuz Ripper,
   He was a filthy nipper.
   He made a pass with broken glass
   An' circumcised the skipper.

# Turalai

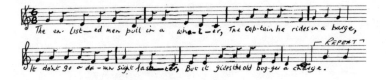

1. The enlisted men pull in a whaler,
   The captain he rides in a barge,
   It don't go a damn sight faster,
   But it gives the old bugger a charge.

*Singing, Turalai, uralai, uralai, Turalai, uralai, aye,*
*Turalai, uralai, uralai, Turalai, uralai, aye.*

2.  The enlisted men pull in a whaler,
    The admiral rides in a gig.
    He don't go a damn sight faster,
    But it makes the old bugger feel big.

3.  The enlisted men eat on the gundecks,
    But the captain don't eat with the mob.
    It ain't that he eats any better,
    He don't want us to know he's a slob.

4.  The enlisted men sleep in their hammocks,
    The captain he sleeps in a bed.
    It ain't that he sleeps any better,
    But he's twenty feet nearer the head.

5.  Now the sexual life of a camel
    Is not quite what everyone thinks.
    One night in an excess of passion,
    He tried to screw the old Sphinx.

6.  Now the Sphinx's posterior regions
    Are clogged by the sands of the Nile,
    Which accounts for the hump on the camel,
    And the Sphinx's inscrutable smile.

7.  In the process of civilization
    From anthropoid ape down to man,
    The palm is awarded the Navy,
    For buggering whatever it can.

8.  Further experimentation
    Has incontrovertibly shown
    That comparative safety on shipboard
    Is enjoyed by the hedgehog alone.

# We Set Sail

1. First we set sail for the Canaries,
   With a cargo of forty-seven fairies.
   We laid about the bunks
   With those forty-seven punks
   Till all our teeth sprouted caries.
       *Bum, bum, bum; bum, bum, bum;*
       *That's how we set sail!*

2. Then we set sail for the Antipodonies,
   With a cargo of forty-seven ponies.
   We horsed about till dawn,
   Till our instruments were worn,
   An' they looked just like melted macaroni.

3. An' then we set sail for the Antilles,
   An' the super-cargo's name it wuz Achilles.
   He gave the crew a feel
   Of his damned erotic eel,
   An' he gave all the orficers the willies.

4. An' then we set sail for the Hawaiians,
   With a cargo of forty-seven lions.
   By the time we had done,
   We had buggered everyone,
   An' the offspring were a miracle to science.

5. An' then we set sail for the Aleutians,
   With a cargo of forty-seven Rooshians.
   By the time we reached the isles,
   They were tangled up in piles,
   An' the rest ended up in institutions.

# Winnipeg Whore

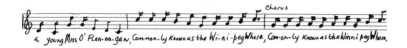

1. My first trip up the Chipaway River,
   My first trip to Canadian shore,
   'Twas there I met a young Miss O'Flannagan,
   Commonly known as the Winnipeg Whore.
      *Commonly known as the Winnipeg Whore.*

2. Well, sez she to me, 'I think I love you
   Let me sit upon your knee.
   How's about a little lovin'.'
   A-dollar-and-a-half is the usual fee.
      *A-dollar-and-a-half is the usual fee.*

3. Well, I took her arm an' she lead me quickly
   Up to the place she used for sleep,
   Dirty old room with a straw-filled mattress,
   Wasn't too clean but it shore wuz cheap.
      *Wasn't too clean but it shore wuz cheap.*

4. Oh, she wuz as slick as a slip'ry elm,
   I didn't know what she wuz about,
   Until I missed my watch and my wallet,
   'Holy Moses!' I called out.
      *'Holy Moses!' I called out.*

5. Then up ran the whores and the sons of the bitches,
   Up to the tune of forty or more,
   Left my clothes, my shoes and my britches,
   While I high-tailed it out of that door.
      *While I high-tailed it out of that door.*

6. Yes, in Winnipeg I learned my lesson,
   I learned it good cos I learned it there.
   If you got a visit a Winnipeg whore,

*Better make sure that you visit her bare.*
  *Better make sure that you visit her bare.* [Shouted].

# You're a Liar

1. Three old whores from Winnipeg
   Drinking their sherry wine,
   Sez one of them to the other two,
   'Yours are smaller than mine.'
       *So pick up yer sheets, me hearties,*
       *Water the decks wi' brine.*
       *Lay to the oars, you lousy whores,*
       *None is bigger than mine!*

2. 'Yer a liar,' sez the other old whore.
   'Mine's as big as the sea.
   A battleship sailed in an' out,
   And it niver bothered me.'

3. 'Yer a liar,' sez the other old whore.
   'Mine's as big as the moon.
   They sail in on the first of the year
   An' niver come out until June.'

4. 'Yer a liar,' sez the other old whore.
   'Mine's as big as the air.
   The ships sail out an' the ships sail in
   An' niver tickle a hair.'

5. 'Yer a liar,' sez the first again.
   'I'd blush to be so small.
   Many's the fleet that sailed right in
   An' niver came out at all.'

# 10   In Conclusion

No collection of music of the sea would be complete without that most solemn piece of all, the sailors' hymn 'Eternal Father'. Whether it is sung by divisions of blue-jackets drawn up on the quarterdeck on Sunday morning or by a gathering of bare-headed merchant seamen paying a last farewell to a messmate as he slides to his final rest over the ship's side far away from home, or whether it is sung in a small village church far removed from the sea by cherubic-faced choirboys to a congregation of country folk, it is acknowledged to be one of the most moving pieces of solemn music.

It is fitting that this hymn should conclude this work, as it is a perpetual reminder that, no matter what man's great technological progress may have been, the sea and the wind do not recognize his puny efforts. New generations of ships and men will come and go, even life itself, but the sea is ageless and its power a timeless challenge to each succeeding generation.

## Eternal Father!

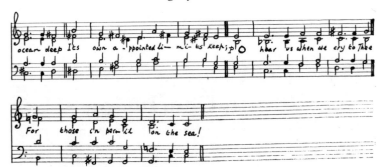

1. Eternal Father! strong to save,
   Whose arm doth bind the restless wave,
   Who bidd'st the mighty ocean deep
   Its own appointed limits keep:
       O hear us when we cry to Thee
       For those in peril on the sea!

2. O Saviour! Whose almighty word
   The winds and waves submissive heard,
   Who walkedst on the foaming deep
   And calm amid its rage didst sleep:
       O hear us when we cry to Thee
       For those in peril on the sea!

3. O Sacred Spirit! Who didst brood
   Upon the chaos dark and rude,
   Who bad'st its angry tumult cease,
   And gavest light, and life, and peace:
       O hear us when we cry to Thee
       For those in peril on the sea!

4. O Trinity of love and power!
   Our brethren shield in danger's hour;
   From rock and tempest, fire and foe,
   Protect them wheresoe'er they go;
       And ever let there rise to Thee
       Glad hymns of praise from land and sea.

# Glossary

# Glossary

| | |
|---|---|
| Abaft | To the rear or nearer to the stern of the ship, i.e. 'The wheel is abaft the main mast.' |
| Acushla | Irish for 'Sweetheart'. |
| Bar | A serious shallowing of the sea off a harbour or estuary entrance. To be avoided at all costs in onshore winds. |
| Belay | Stop, make fast. |
| Belaying Pin | A shaped wooden or metal pin having a large diameter upper part and tapering to its lower extremity which fits into a hole in the pin rail. It is used for making a rope secure by passing it in the form of a figure of eight alternately round the pin on top and beneath the rail. Instant release is made by wrenching the pin out of its socket. |
| Block | A hard wood shell (later iron) containing revolving sheaves (dished wheels) round which ropes run. Sometimes used singly to direct the pull on a rope they are often used in unison to form part of a purchase or tackle. |
| Bower anchor | Main anchor. |
| Bousing Down (Bowsing) | To haul a rope down tight and belay it (secure it). |

187

| | |
|---|---|
| Bowsprit | A boom or spar projecting forward of the stem at a raised angle. Used for fitting fore-and-aft stays to the foremast and for securing jibs and forestay sails. |
| Brace | A tackle secured to the yards for hauling them round to trim the sails to the wind. 'Bracing the yards'. |
| Buntline | Ropes made fast to the foot of a square sail, led up to the yard then after passing through blocks going down to the deck. Used for hauling the sail up to the yard when stowing it away (in harbour). There are usually two buntlines on each side of the sail. |
| Capstan | A vertical barrel operated by pushing wooden bars inserted in sockets round the top of the barrel. The lower edge of the barrel was fitted with pawls working into a rack to prevent the barrel slipping back when the heaving stopped. Primarily used for heaving home the anchor, it was often used in conjunction with the horizontal windlass for moving heavy loads or hoisting yards. |
| Careenage | A place where a ship can be heeled over so that a part of the underwater hull is lifted above water for examination, cleaning, antifouling or repairs. |
| Cathead | A wooden, sometimes metal, construction projecting out from either side of the forecastle head of a ship. Fitted with sheaves it was used to lift the anchor so that it could be made fast horizontally outside the rail of the forecastle head and |

secured temporarily for letting go later. Called cathead from the practice of carving a cat's or lion's head on the outboard butt end.

Chequerboard watch A ship was divided into two watches. Where mixed crews were used (common on ships working to and from the West Indies) one watch would be all black the other all white. This tended to prevent friction and engender friendly rivalry.

Chesstree Not in use in the later sailing ships but present in ships of the eighteenth and early nineteenth centuries. A wooden block with several sheaves attached to the bulwarks, deck or forecastle head, through which the tack of the foresail or mainsail was rove (threaded) for heaving down the weather clew.

Chowlat Slang for a concoction of food – a stew.

Clew The lower corners of a square sail. Also the after lower corner of a fore-and-aft sail. The corners have a thimble/s (metal-lined eye) to which the sheet is attached.

Clipper A type of fast sailing ship – *Cutty Sark* now on show at Greenwich is a fine example. Revolutionizing traditional ship design they were finer in the beam with sharp stems and tapering long run aft to streamlined sterns. They minimized on drag, the main obstacle to speed, and set towering clouds of sail on skyscraping masts. They were employed in trade that made every voyage a race

|  |  |
|---|---|
| | across the southern oceans, tea from China and wool from Australia. |
| Course | The name given to the lowest square sail on a mast of a square-rigged sailing-ship. Fore course – the lowest square sail set on the foremost mast. Main course – lowest on the main mast. |
| Davit | A curved steel projection with a tackle fitted at its head used in pairs for lifting boats from their chocks on the boat deck and swinging them over the side ready for lowering into the water. |
| Dog-watches | Two two-hour watches (4 p.m. to 6 p.m. and 6 p.m. until 8 p.m.) are known as the first and second dog-watch. Introduced into the two-watch system in order to change the times of the night watches. During the second dog-watch no work other than trimming sails and yards was done allowing for a sing-song to a fu-fu band, yarning, or simply resting. |
| Donkey Engine | Not the ship's main propulsion engine but a small steam-driven engine used for lifting or hauling or operating the windlass or capstan. |
| Down Wind | Running before the wind, i.e. with the wind astern. |
| Drogher | Sailing-ships employed in the timber trade between Canada and the UK. Timber droghers were unusual in that they loaded the huge baulks of timber through doors cut into the bows. |
| Fireship's Crew | The female 'crew' of a dockside brothel. |
| Flying Jib | The foremost and lightest of the jibs |

|                    |                                                                                                                                                                                                          |
| ------------------ | -------------------------------------------------------------------------------------------------------------------------------------------------------------------------------------------------------- |
|                    | (there could be up to five) and set out on the extremity of the jib-boom.                                                                                                                                |
| Forebitts          | A place on the foredeck where vertical baulks of timber protruded to which ropes, warps, halyards, even the anchor cable, could be secured.                                                                |
| Forecastle         | Always pronounced as 'Fo'c's'le', the forward part of the vessel extending into the bow where the crew ate and slept.                                                                                     |
| Foredeck           | Forward decking leading towards the bow.                                                                                                                                                                  |
| Foremast           | Foremost mast.                                                                                                                                                                                           |
| Foresail           | Foremost sail.                                                                                                                                                                                           |
| Futtock Shrouds    | Short steel bars or wires connecting the lower ends of the topmast rigging to the top of the lower mast below.                                                                                             |
| Galley             | An open boat using oars for propulsion, sails were sometimes used. Also the kitchen of a ship where food was cooked.                                                                                      |
| Gantline           | A single rope passed through a block fixed high above the deck, used for hoisting sails aloft ready for bending to a spar, or for lifting any gear for use aloft.                                          |
| Gasket             | A small length of rope fitted to the jackstay (handrail) of a yard of a square-rigged ship for the purpose of securing the sails after they had been rolled up.                                           |
| Go about           | Change direction – to change tacks when beating to windward.                                                                                                                                             |
| Halyard            | A 'haul-yard' – a rope with which to haul a yard up the mast. Nowadays a rope to haul a sail up the mast.                                                                                                 |
| Hawse              | The part of the bow of a ship pierced by hawse holes which enable the                                                                                                                                    |

| | |
|---|---|
| | anchor hawser (cable) to run out to the anchor. |
| Hawser | A large diameter rope (usually coir) or wire used for towing or as an additional rope for mooring. |
| Horse Latitudes | The area in the North Atlantic between the north-east trade winds and the westerly winds – between latitudes 30° and 35° North. An area of prolonged calms and light winds but without the heavy rains of the doldrums. The name originates from the time sailing-ships made prolonged passages and horses died on board reaching the limits of their endurance around these latitudes. |
| Hoy | A small craft used as a carrier to water or victual a larger vessel at sea. |
| Jackscrew | Implement as its name implies to 'screw' bales of cotton tightly into the more inaccessible corners of a ship. Often used carelessly into cramming the hold too tightly with cotton which expanded when wet causing planks to spring, causing the cotton to expand even more and the ship to founder usually in mid-ocean with the loss of all hands. |
| Jib-boom | A long tapering boom projecting out beyond the bowsprit to which the flying jib is secured. |
| Knightheads | The top of two heavy sections of timber that are built up and protrude on either side of the stem to support the bowsprit in sailing-ships. |
| Larboard | Old version of portside. |
| Lazaret | The provision storeroom in a sailing-ship, situated aft and entered down a ladder from the pantry. |
| Lighter | Where deeply laden ships cannot |

enter a shallow harbour they are 'lightened' by much smaller and shallower vessels removing the cargo and transporting ashore. The 'lightening' craft are referred to as lighters.

| | |
|---|---|
| Liner | A passenger or cargo ship sailing on an advertised regular run. |
| Luff | The forward edge of a triangular fore-and-aft sail (the edge nearest to the stay to which it is attached). |
| To luff | To luff is to bring a ship up into the wind by putting the helm down, the helmsman always stood on the weather (windward) side of the helm. The manoeuvre spilled wind from the sails when a vessel was being overpressed by a squall of wind or when it was necessary to slow the vessel down or stop her. |
| Marlin Spike | A pointed steel spike used by the sailmaker for splicing. The lay of the rope is opened by pushing the spike between the strands so that further strands can be interlaced to complete the splice. |
| Messenger | A thin line thrown ashore or to another vessel so that a heavier, less manageable cable or hawser can be hove across. |
| Molly Hawks | Fulmars or storm petrels. Small birds with powerful wings which frequent the 'Roaring Forties' and high thirty latitudes of the southern oceans. Often referred to as Mother Carey's Chickens. |
| Nipper | Young boys (powder-monkeys when at action stations) whose duty it was when the ship was heaving anchor to 'nip' or secure the |

indrawn cable to a continuous rope linked between two capstans in order to haul it aft to the cable tier.

Old Man
Captain

Orlop
The lowest deck in a three-deck ship usually used for the stowage of cables and other heavy or infrequently used objects.

Packet
Fast sailing-ships contracted to carry mail in the eighteenth century. Falmouth packets carried cargo, passengers and mail across the North Atlantic, Harwich packets plied the same trade to Ostend and The Hook of Holland.

Pawl
A metal tooth which drops into a recess at the base of a capstan or a recess cut horizontally into the barrel of a windlass to prevent the drum from spinning back. When heaving in the cable the pawls drop into the recesses with a succession of clacks. The old capstan shanty quotes, 'Heave around the capstan gain a pawl', i.e. to gain another few inches.

Powder-monkeys
Very young boys enlisted in men-of-war whose duty it was to carry the gun powder charges to the guns when engaged in battle.

Quadrant
The forerunner of today's sextant for taking altitudes of heavenly bodies for computing a ship's position. Invented in 1730, it consisted of an eighth of a circle (45°) and using a double reflection, measured angles up to 90°.

The quadrant is also part of a ship's steering gear. It is a large piece of metal in the shape of a

| | sector of a circle connected to the rudder head. The steering chains which are connected to the wheel are fitted on the quadrant. |
|---|---|
| Ringbolt | A heavy metal ring secured to a short length of medium-sized rope and fixed to the deck. Used for wrapping round and round a larger rope (warp or hawse) to hold it while it is shifted from windlass or capstan to make it fast permanently on the bitts. |
| Rocker Bar | Long handles attached to the 'Jiggety Pump' which the crew threw their weight down on and raised alternatively to pump the ship clear of water. |
| Rudder | A flat frame fastened vertically and hinged to the stern post of a ship which controls the direction of movement when under way. |
| Scouse | Deriving from Liverpool. A concoction of fried-up left-overs. |
| Scuppers | A number of holes at the joining of the bulwarks and deck to permit rapid shedding of water over the side in heavy weather. |
| Sheaves | The small wheels in a block. |
| Sheet | A rope (or wire) attached to the bottom corner of sails and used to trim to gain the best advantage from the wind. |
| Shellback | A nickname for a sailor used by landsmen. |
| Skysail | The highest sail that could be set in a square-rigged ship. Usually set by the fast clippers racing for markets in the wool and tea trade. |
| Spar | Describes a long piece of wood. Usually refers to mast furniture such |

|  |  |
|---|---|
| | as booms or yards. |
| Square Rigger | A ship rigged with sails set square on yards across the masts. |
| Tack | The lower corner or clew on the weather side of the lowest square sail on a mast. Also the name of the rope by which the clew is hauled down. |
| To tack | To go about when beating to windward. To push the helm down and turn the ship's head through the eye of the wind. |
| Taffrail | The rail, usually varnished teak and decorated, acting as a capping on the bulwarks surrounding the stern of a ship. |
| Tall Ship | Originally a square-rigged sailing-ship. Today's derivative embraces sailing-ships which are fore-and-aft rigged and come together in a brotherhood of national goodwill as sail-training vessels. |
| Trim Sail | To set the sails so as to take advantage of the changing slant or changing power of the wind. A constant and back-breaking task when beating to windward in the northern latitudes. |
| 'Tween Decks | Originally 'Between Deck's but corrupted with usage. In sailing-ships it was the decking of the hold. Tween decks is the space between the tween deck and the decking above it, usually the main deck. |
| Up Wind | With the wind ahead. A vessel to windward is a ship on the weather side. |
| Warp | A large rope used for heaving or 'warping' a ship from one place to another (between dockside berths etc). The name of a rope connecting |

| | |
|---|---|
| | the anchor to the ship. |
| Watch | In sailing-ships two watches were kept, each watch of four hours except the two-hour dog-watches. Those on duty were known as the watch on deck. Those off duty as the watch below. The captain would take one watch with the second mate in charge of the deck, the other being the first mate's watch. The watches were carried on without respite seven days a week for the duration of the cruise. |
| Whelp | Wooden (later metal) vertical strips fitted to the barrel of a capstan or windlass to prevent the rope turns taken round it from slipping. |
| Whip | To bind the end of a piece of rope to stop it fraying. |
| Windlass | A machine set in the bow of a vessel used for heaving in the anchor cable consisting of a horizontal drum around which the cable was wound and rotated by men using hand spikes or bars. |
| Yard | A wooden (or steel) spar hoisted horizontally across a mast. A square sail is secured across the yard to hang down below it. |
| Yard Arm | The extreme tips of the above-mentioned yard. |

# Indexes

# Index of Titles and First Lines

# Subject Index